DISCARD

Atoms for Peace

· · · · · · ·

Also by David O. Woodbury

Atoms
for
Peace

by David O. Woodbury

illustrated by Henry Bugbee Kane

WITH NEW MATERIAL
ON RECENT DEVELOPMENTS

DODD, MEAD & COMPANY   •   NEW YORK

• • •

To
The Men and Women
Who Courageously Opened
Pandora's Box
And So Created
The Atomic Age

• • •

Foreword

· · · ·

THERE IS nothing more exciting or bewildering in the writing game than to tackle a subject that is changing day by day—a field in which anything may become obsolete overnight, in which new principles come up as fast and as unexpectedly as mushrooms.

Such a subject is atomic energy. In this book I have tried to present a picture of the way things are now, with a few glimpses of more distant vistas of the future. Looking ahead is the tricky part of it. Nobody, not even the most responsible insider, knows how the future will shape up or how fast it will overtake us.

The presence of this grand gamble as a controlling factor in so large an undertaking as atomic development, tends to make gamblers of the participants themselves—sportsmen in the sense that their plans and calculations may have to be changed at a moment's notice as the fanciful pattern of atomic history unfolds. The men who can do this on so high an intellectual level are interesting indeed, and it is to them that I am indebted for many of the lively guesses and prognostications in the following pages.

It is difficult to give proper acknowledgment to all those who have willingly discussed with me their work and their hopes in the atomic field. There are too many of them. If I single out a few, it must not be interpreted as indicating that the help of many others was not fully as valuable.

The *facts* of the book have been obtained largely from published material, and with the generous help and support of our government people in Washington and at the Argonne and Brookhaven National Laboratories. It is the inspiration, the spirit, that came mainly from individuals—such men as Dr. Walter Zinn at Argonne, Dr. Chauncey Starr at North American Aviation, Drs. Cipriani, Gilbert and Keys of the Canadian project at Chalk River. Their outlook on our atomic future is uniformly hopeful, eager, even joyful. No one could talk to them for long without realizing that the world will be all right if it will only consent to continue on the constructive side which they represent. It is the willfully destructive, the everything's-been-done and the downright ignorant attitudes which can lead to trouble. I don't believe these attitudes will win. The world's constructive minds are too vigorous and too inventive to let that happen.

In the growth of any art as far-reaching as nuclear science there is bound to be controversy, and of course there is the bomb and the constant threat of newer and more awful bombs. In general, I have done as well as I can to avoid these controversies, especially those concerned with economics and politics, believing that the present writing should be a statement of fact and probability rather than guess and opinion. The interesting and inspiring thing in the atomic picture is that, though people may differ widely as to how advances should be applied, few quarrel with the ultimate objective of peace and a better world for all. Method rather than goal is in argument.

I imagine that these differences will eventually be resolved, though not without mistakes and serious delays as wrong paths are followed and abandoned. But in the end, if the atom has a service to render mankind, it will render it. How soon it will do so depends on how few are our mistakes and how short our delays. The way to cut them down lies through knowledge and interest, which this book seeks, in its modest way, to increase.

DAVID O. WOODBURY

Contents

. . . .

PART ONE
· · · · ·

Atomic Power
Is on the Way

I. Dawn at Midnight

• • • • • • • •

I WAS SUDDENLY broad awake.

It was full daylight in our California bedroom, yet the clock above the door indicated 4:20 of a midwinter night. My wife was already sitting up in bed.

"Something is wrong," she whispered, hastily putting a toe onto the floor. I leaped out too, taking another quick glance at the clock. It hadn't stopped. The second hand was moving as calmly as usual, although it looked a little redder than it ought. Was something afire?

We met at the window facing the east and thrust the curtains aside. There was no fire. A beautiful rosy dawn had burst over the mountain wall above us, bringing full daylight to our yard. You could count the blossoms on the orange trees.

"It's the end of the world," she breathed foolishly.

"It's something," I whispered back, as foolishly.

We stood, arms around each other, facing the mystery, groping in our minds as people will for an adjustment to something that can't be so.

Then, as we stared, the "dawn" began to recede, closing down little by little on the mountains till their blackness blended with the night again. The stars came out, one by one, just as they do when dusk falls. Around the edges and then toward the middle they blinked into view reassuringly. The

3

galloping shadow of the mountain rim showed just barely against the deep indigo of the east.

"What happened?" She was shaking and so was I. We stood holding onto each other for a long moment to make sure it wouldn't happen again.

We thought we had dreamed it and started to relax when the earthquake hit us. It was not to be mistaken for any dream, least of all by a Californian. The house rocked sideways till the clock banged on the wall. Dishes tinkled distantly in the kitchen. There was quiet for some seconds, then a second weaker shake rumbled the big window in the living room. A third and a fourth growled briefly at even intervals. The mechanical precision of the thing cohered my senses.

"It's that atom bomb over in Nevada!" I cried, fully awake at last. We laughed and went back to bed.

In this homely little scene two ordinary citizens of the U.S.A. had experienced the might of the atom. I knew, of course, that the Atomic Energy Commission was putting on a series of tests at Yucca Flat, east of Las Vegas, but I'd ignored it. Too far away to get up for in the middle of the night, and nothing to see anyway. Yucca Flat is 256 miles from us, by airline distance. Nobody had suggested that the explosion would produce full daylight on the Pacific Coast and turn people out of bed.

To us, this startling first-hand experience with atomic energy was more impressive, and certainly more sobering, than the far greater explosions that have been set off since in the Pacific. It happened to *us*. It blasted peaceful citizens out of a sound sleep and sent them to the window, shaking. It cracked the concrete floor of their hobby shop. The detonation of a spoonful of atoms 256 miles away had shattered their complacency with a demonstration whose violence was not to be forgotten.

4

Perhaps it would be a good thing if such an awakening could come to every American—a reveille that would alert us all to the new day of atomic power. For, whether we realize it or not, we are 13 years deep in the Atomic Age, and its hold on us is already as grim and as permanent as death. Or, as this book intends to show, as powerful and as deathless as life itself.

America enjoys sensation. It likes to skip from one breathless experience to another, skimming the cream, then forgetting. Nobody wants to think over the meaning of the various crises in the intervals between.

But the meaning of atomic energy is not to be dealt with in a mere series of front-page sensation stories. There is much thinking to be done outside the laboratories and the Government agencies. It is the kind of thinking the world began to do when Columbus told of discovering a new hemisphere, when Marconi spanned the Atlantic with invisible waves of intelligence, when Edison light shamed its first gas lamp in the city of New York, when the first automobile frightened its first horse. It is a kind of thinking a whole people has to do, pursuant to its privilege of running its own lives; the kind of thinking that goes into helping a son or daughter wisely choose a profession, the kind that determines the major trends of business.

The atom is for everybody—inescapable, vital, a turning point in human affairs.

If the realization of atomic power had come slowly, over fifty years, as most great discoveries do, there might have been less obligation upon the common citizen to participate. But bursting suddenly upon us, its impact on national thought is quite as great as its effect upon science. War unleashed a new giant which peace must tame.

So great are the problems of the atom's incredible power that scientists and statesmen alone cannot cope with them.

The nations most likely to survive are those which have accelerated their everyday understanding of these problems, facing them candidly as a whole people.

The atomic force is by far the greatest that has ever come over the horizons of man. It can be tamed—that has been shown—but it won't be tamed unless knowledge replaces ignorance and indifference. Technical knowledge is not enough; it is only a dangerous boast. The atom must be woven into the fabric of the nation as completely as the telephone.

The problems of the atom are incredibly difficult because its force is of a totally new order of magnitude, yet they are being solved at a speed never before matched in science. When a little group of men set the first chain reaction going under the stadium at Stagg Field, in 1942, nothing was known for sure. Today, only 13 years later, vast areas have already been explored; a great body of knowledge has been gathered, processes of amazing complexity are understood and utilized.

This unique achievement is not only a legacy of war; it is a sudden flowering of the slow, careful centuries of growth of the scientific method. True, the emergency telescoped years of effort into months and days, but once over, the pace did not greatly slacken. The attack upon the problems of the atom is still as concentrated, as brilliant, as fast-moving as ever.

In the atomic age science has crossed a frontier into a region of vastly accelerated progress. Can the same be said of the world in general?

One of the saddest elements in our situation today is the sickening contrast between knowledge and ignorance. We surround ourselves with mechanisms of beautiful effectiveness and fantastic complication, for we have a great genius for understanding nature and enlisting her help. We safely entrust our lives to machines of every description which depend upon the faultless working of hundreds of natural laws we have correctly interpreted. Yet we cannot govern ourselves effectively; we cannot even conduct our adult lives or educate our children or control our criminals effectively. After millenniums of struggle we still make the same social mistakes. Human lessons taught times without number we still refuse to learn.

Somehow, scientific knowledge and know-how seem to be able to live side by side with human blundering and ignorance. But they live in a union so dangerous that we are forever on the brink of extinction.

It is something for every man to ponder, this chasm between our mechanical perfection and our mental incompetence —as a civilization. When people accuse science of irresponsibility, for filling the world with machines too frightening to live with, they forget that it is the other side of the equation that is really at fault. It is ignorance and indifference that are dangerous, not knowledge and dedication.

In the atomic age these incompatible bedfellows can no longer sleep side by side. "Wise up or blow up" is the crude formula by which we must live.

2. Approach to Peace
. . . .

THIS IS the thought, I think, that lay behind President Eisenhower's dramatic offer before the United Nations to share the peaceful atom with the rest of the world. On December 8, 1953, he spoke some of the most ringing words ever uttered on the threat and promise of the atom. Having painted the terrors of the bombs in vivid language, he summed them up thus:

"Let no one think that the expenditure of vast sums for weapons and systems of defense can guarantee absolute safety for the cities and citizens of any nation. The awful arithmetic of the atomic bomb does not permit of any such easy solution. Even against the most powerful defense an aggressor in possession of the effective minimum number of atomic bombs for a surprise attack could probably place a sufficient number of his bombs on the chosen targets to cause hideous damage.

Should such an atomic attack be launched against the United States, our reactions would be swift and resolute. But for me to say that the defense capabilities of the United States are such that they could inflict terrible losses upon an aggressor —for me to say that the retaliation capabilities of the United States are so great that such an aggressor's land would be laid waste—all this, while fact, is not the true expression of the purpose and the hope of the United States.

8

To pause there would be to confirm the hopeless finality of a belief that two atomic colossi are doomed malevolently to eye each other indefinitely across a trembling world. . . .

My country's purpose is to help us move out of the dark chamber of horrors into the light, to find a way by which the minds of men everywhere can move forward toward peace and happiness and well being. . . .

It is not enough to take this weapon out of the hands of the soldiers. It must be put into the hands of those who will know how to strip its military casing and adapt it to the arts of peace. . . .

I therefore make the following proposals:

The Governments principally involved, to the extent permitted by elementary prudence, to begin now and continue to make joint contributions from their stockpiles of normal uranium and fissionable materials to an International Atomic Energy Agency.

Undoubtedly initial and early contributions to this plan would be small in quantity. However, the proposal has the great virtue that it can be undertaken without the irritations and mutual suspicions incident to any attempt to set up a completely acceptable system of world-wide inspection and control.

The more important responsibility of this Atomic Energy Agency would be to devise methods whereby this fissionable material would be allocated to serve the peaceful pursuits of mankind. Experts would be mobilized to apply atomic energy to the needs of agriculture, medicine and other peaceful activities. A special purpose would be to provide abundant electrical energy in the power-starved areas of the world. . . .

The coming months will be fraught with fateful decisions. In this Assembly; in the capitals and military headquarters of the world; in the hearts of men everywhere, be they governors or governed, may they be the decisions which will lead this world out of fear and into peace. The United States pledges . . . to devote its entire heart and mind to find the way by which the miraculous inventiveness of man shall not be dedicated to his death, but consecrated to his life."

This was a grand concept and was acknowledged as such by all the free world.

The purpose of this book is to provide the background which any citizen must have in order to appreciate his responsibility and his privilege in helping the inspiring words of the President to come true.

In sounding this dramatic note before the whole world the President had several carefully planned objectives. The first was to establish an official measure of the penalty for aggression: annihilation without the possibility of victory. The second was to let the world know that the benefits of atomic energy can be so decisive as to bring about a revolution in world relationships. And the third: that there is work which atomic power can do now, immediately, in rescuing backward countries from famine and low standards of living.

The President believed the peacetime promise of the atom so great that he was willing to pledge his country's efforts to set up a world bank of atomic fuel. His convictions were so strong that he made a deliberate challenge to all nations to co-operate in applying the atom to benign uses, under rules which should be uniform everywhere.

The more we examine Eisenhower's motives in making this offer the deeper they go. Most laymen so far have been preoccupied with the bomb, mainly because data on military uses have been the only material available, and because only the bomb has been considered dramatic enough for mention in the press. In his attempt to move the world into the atomic future he officially left military preoccupation behind, implying that just as much drama and excitement could be gleaned from the good uses of the atom as from the bad.

In the following pages I shall try to present, intelligibly, the background of the atomic art, and to build out from that with informed guesses as to the future. An exciting feature of this attempt is that it would be difficult to predict too wildly, once the basic facts are understood. We in America are insatiably inventive. Never has there been such an opportunity for so many naturally talented minds to venture on a great voyage of exploration. Given the start we already have it is certain that advances will come thick and fast, and that profound changes will take place in our way of life within the lifetimes of most people now living.

As the President said, it is a choice between annihilation and a new life. Never before has civilization been confronted by two such absolute alternatives. The choice has to be made. If it is for peace—and we are willing to work hard enough to insure it—we shall leap sharply upward into a world of greater comfort and happiness, better health and security. If it is for war—and we are too lazy or too ignorant to prevent it—then, short of wiping out the human race altogether, we may well set it back into the dark ages to be begun all over again.

In this roundup of atomic facts the reader and I are in nearly the same position. I do not have access to much inside information; that is, to classified material. Like the reader, I know only what I read and what I can learn from the insiders who are at liberty to tell me only what is already in the public domain. What little advantage I have derives from having taken the time to go as deeply into the subject as any layman reporter can.

The material brought to light in this book, I hope, will give the answers to a layman's kind of question: What is it all about? Why does it work that way? How does it affect me? Atomic energy, technically, is beyond my comprehension as it is beyond most of yours. Thus the questions and their answers remain rather general, and always in some way related to our common lives.

Before going on to consider peaceful atomic power there is a word to be said about atomic war. It would probably not be as horrible as many excited people think. Principally, it would be more "efficient,"—a conflict enormously speeded up by the use of the new mass weapon. Everything would happen at once. For the first time in history virtually every citizen would be on the battle line. The action would be intense, and then it would be over.

We have confused the imagined horrors of atomic attack with the staggering number of people directly affected. We have identified the atomic horror with the idea of American cities being laid in ruins and American people slaughtered by the tens of thousands, as if all this were something peculiar to the atom.

But is it? If Detroit were hit by an atom bomb, or by several, the results would be different only in degree from those of the bombing of London and many European cities with TNT in the last war. In fact, there is something to be said for the atomic weapon since it would wipe out its target far more cleanly and swiftly than lesser weapons were able to do. There would be no waiting in terror for enemy planes to come over, no long horror, repeated month after month, of cowering in bomb shelters. There would probably be very little maiming and dismemberment. It would be decisive; one would either be dead or unharmed.

Admiral William F. Halsey said recently that he thought there was too much hysteria about the H-bomb. "I can't see the difference," he remarked, "between being killed by an H-bomb or a hand grenade."

We are so excited mainly because, for the first time, modern war would seek us out here, at home. We have thought of ourselves as suppliers of men and materials for other people's wars. Now it looks as if we might have one of our own. In the end, are we likely to suffer any differently or any more than the Londoners and Berliners did?

Atomic death, as I shall describe later, is, if anything, less painful and less horrible than death by maiming or by incineration. If we can take the destruction of Hiroshima and Nagasaki as valid examples, a mass of people takes it rather remarkably in stride. Those who survive go about the work of cleaning up the ruins with amazing energy and courage. They do so, at least, in the knowledge that the attack is over and will not be repeated.

Atomic attack, one may believe, is something like being hit by a tornado. It happens so fast that its victims do not have time to fear it very much. When it is over they are free to right themselves without the panic and hysteria incident to war by attrition.

This is not to argue that atomic destruction in America would not be a horrible thing. All war is terrifying, whatever the weapon. If we are to avoid such horror we would do well to fix our attention on the forces that constantly lead toward war and eliminate them. We should be fighting an offensive, now; an offensive against the ideas and sophistries that seek to justify aggression, and that seek to divert our attention from the danger of conquest.

We are a nation that *talks* poorly but *does* well. We had better get started on the doing before it is too late.

This, in effect, is what President Eisenhower indicated in his proposed bridge between nations built out of atoms at work. By withdrawing even a small part of international attention from atomic war and fixing it upon atomic peace, he felt that the chances of war might be reduced. If America acts soon enough and decisively enough, he implied, a future war might be impossible.

3. What Is Energy?

• • • • • • •

OF ALL the benefits that atomic energy will bring to man the most valuable to the people will be power.

The march of civilization through the centuries has been accompanied by a gradual increase in the use of energy, until today all peoples measure their standard of living by it. Energy, the capacity to do work that is bound up in fuel, holds the key to progress. Modern civilization would not be possible without it.

Primitive man possessed no more than the energy he could store in his own muscles by eating food. It was little, hardly enough to keep him alive and to hold his enemies at bay.

Eventually he discovered fire and unlocked the chemical energy of combustion. He understood it poorly at first and it merely warmed him and cooked his food. After a long while he learned to smelt a few metals with it, separating iron and copper from their ores and then tin, reheating them to forge simple implements of bronze and wrought iron, such as knives and spears. Some time later the energy of fire gave him light.

Meanwhile, he had captured a new store of energy in the muscles of animals and could plow and drag loads. And he had

14

learned to use the force of the wind to drive his ships across the sea.

With these few simple types of energy civilization drifted through scores of centuries, benighted and essentially miserable. It was not until a few hundred years ago that an expanding knowledge of the forces of nature opened the eyes of the world to the real meaning of energy. It began to be apparent that progress depended on it.

Energy, power and work are the three terms that have to do with the utilization of natural forces, and they are easily confused. They have exact meanings to scientific people but are used loosely and often interchangeably by the rest of us. Simply stated, energy is the ability to do work; work is what results when energy is put into action; power is the rate at which the work is done.

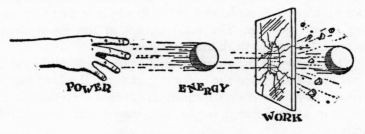

Energy has two forms: potential and kinetic. Potential energy is that which is not at the moment in use. It is in storage, waiting until some trigger is pushed and it is released to perform work. A charged storage battery holds potential energy in chemical form; so does a flashlight cell when the light is not burning. On being connected by wires to some kind of useful device, the energy within each appears as electric current and work is done: a starting motor is spun, a small bulb is made to glow.

Energy is not lost by being used; it is merely transformed.

The work that a starting motor does in a car results in storing most of the original energy as mechanical motion in the moving parts of the motor, with a little thrown away as heat. The work that electricity does in a flashlight provides illumination and heat, in this case mostly heat that cannot be recaptured.

All energy attempts to go downhill to a resting place as heat in the surroundings. It cannot be dislodged and made to do more work unless there is another "hill" beyond.

Kinetic energy is merely that which is represented by a body in motion. Even as heat it is still kinetic energy—the minute "thermal" motions of the atoms and molecules. One can think of the air in a room as constantly darting around in random fashion, doing no work because everything in the room remains at the same temperature. When you come in from outdoors on a cold day the warm air inside bombards your skin, does work upon its molecules, sets them to moving faster, and thus warms you up. The total energy in the room hasn't changed, but useful work has been done.

The energy of the atom is stored—potential—and most of it has been there since the beginning of time. If a long line of brilliant physicists hadn't recently discovered a method of releasing it, atomic energy might have stayed locked up indefinitely.

Atomic energy is mainly stored in potential form and one can think of the tiny particles within the atom as if they were the coils of a spring tightly wound up (who wound them, or how, we have little idea). The catch which holds the spring against release is of immense strength and no force on earth seemed great enough to unlatch it. Then at last a peculiar little object called the neutron was discovered, which could easily unfasten the catch of a few heavy atoms like uranium. When the catch is freed the atomic spring unwinds a little. In fact, it is smashed into several smaller springs, and the energy produced turns up as the kinetic energy of the parts flying away from each other. They do no work until they hit something. The art of using atomic energy consists in bombarding other materials with the flying fragments of exploding atoms, heating these materials and then using the heat.

The atomic explosion of a pound of uranium produces more than 2½ million times as much heat energy as the burning of a pound of coal. If one pound of any material could be transformed completely it would produce eleven billion kilowatt-hours of energy—enough to light 100,000 100-watt lamps for a year. So far, science cannot realize anywhere near that. Powerful as it is, the atomic reaction utilizes no more than a thousandth part of the potential energy of the atom. One great field of exploration today seeks to find out how to utilize more.

The term "power," as we said, means the *rate* of doing work. Through association with the adjective "powerful" it has come to be used everywhere to describe force in action—the ability to do work. This slight confusion with the meaning of energy, which is indeed the ability to do work, has given us "electric power," "steam power," "water power," and now "atomic power." So now we have a general term for the capability of getting work done, and though the words are interchanged, the meaning is clear and virile.

Atomic *power*, then, will mean for us the creation of great blocks of electricity or heat to help do the work of the world. Whereas, atomic *energy*, a hazier term, will describe the whole field of the forces which the atom can release.

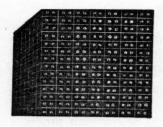

4. We Make a Start

• • • • • • • •

FOR THE first ten years of atomic history, the power side played a minor part. Everything was concentrated on the military side in a headlong race to develop, first the atom bomb and then the hydrogen bomb. It was essential to perfect them to the point where they could become the major weapons in any future world war.

From the beginning, gigantic quantities of electric power have been required to produce the special forms of fuel needed for the bombs. Some of this power, as we shall see later, is recovered as heat as the fuel is prepared. But it is thrown away, because it would be too expensive and too wasteful of time to retrieve it.

In the early 1950's, however, there was reason to believe that the end of the atomic arms race was not far away, at least for the United States. There were enough atomic bombs in sight to fight any conceivable war. The members of the Atomic Energy Commission felt that it was high time to explore the possibilities of atomic power, first to see if peacetime uses existed at all, then to find out whether American industry, particularly the electric power industry, could use atomic power economically.

One major stumbling block that had never before been

encountered in applying a great new discovery, was the blanket of secrecy which shrouded all atomic work. The apparatus for making bomb material and for turning out useful power was essentially the same. Raw uranium was needed for both; even refined and enriched fuel could be switched to either use. Congress and the AEC both were reluctant to create a new industry out of the secret structure which was putting the United States in the forefront of atomic war preparedness. It looked as if it would be impossible to launch private enterprise into atomic power exploration without jeopardizing our position in the atomic weapons race.

The Atomic Energy Act of 1946 specifically prohibited the disclosure of atomic know-how, except to contractors engaged in bomb-making work. It not only forbade key information to be given to the American public, but directed that it be withheld from all the world, including the official atomic scientists of other countries, even those who had been our trusted colleagues during the war.

The Commission, however, took a courageous stand, believing that a separation could be made between the military and peaceful atomic arts. With the approval of the powerful Joint Committee on Atomic Energy in Congress, they invited a number of electric utility groups to study atomic power possibilities and to offer definite suggestions for developing the commercial atomic art. These groups were "cleared" and taken part way behind the secrecy curtain, so that they could obtain enough classified information to make their studies complete.

Four combinations of power company people tackled the problem and spent a number of millions of dollars exploring atomic power on the purely commercial front. After about a year's deliberation they all wrote reports, which were edited of their secret content by the AEC and published. They included complete design and cost studies of large atomic power plants suitable for turning out huge quantities of electricity.

Then, in the summer of 1953, the Joint Committee held a long series of hearings. Hundreds of witnesses were invited to appear, including members of all the groups who had contributed to the power studies.

The result of this was threefold: first, the private companies agreed that the development of atomic power in large stations at the present time could not compete, dollar for dollar, with electricity from standard coal-burning plants. Second, that even if economical atomic power were much nearer commercial realization than it is, the gigantic expense of full-sized plants would be beyond the finances of the power companies alone. Third, however, the witnesses agreed that the future for atomic power was bright and that if the government would start the work with further research and with subsidies, the art might well be set up on a sound commercial basis in the end.

A fourth point which was strongly brought out was that the Atomic Energy Act itself must be liberalized before any real start could be made toward giving the public atomic power. Unless the government proposed to make a monopoly of atomic power as it had done of atomic weapons, the severe restrictions on the right to possess atomic fuel and to use it, must be lifted.

A great deal of credit belongs to the Joint Committee, under the chairmanship of Representative Sterling Cole of New York. They worked hard through the sweltering summer to hear and question every witness who took an interest in the future of atomic power: industrialists, scientists, government officials, labor leaders, advocates of public ownership of utilities. The testimony bulked larger than several books; the consensus overwhelmingly gave approval to an atomic power system owned and operated by private industry.

Encouraged by the great interest shown on all sides, the

committee set about sparking the country's first real atom power project. They were impressed by the eagerness shown by industry to participate in the pioneer stages, though early atomic stations could not possibly compete with steam. The American competitive system was working healthily; business was ready to gamble in a big way on our native ingenuity. It was especially good that the power industry was so enthusiastic. Severely limited by state laws as to profits, these men were taking the long view for the good of the whole nation.

As soon as the hearings were completed in July, 1953, Mr. Cole wrote the AEC, asking it to lay out a plan of action that would lead to full-scale power experiments. A few months later the commission presented a five-year plan for atomic power exploration, to cost about $200 million. Five different types of atomic "pile" or power reactor were proposed.

That plan is now beginning to take shape. The general scheme is to assign the projects to various industrial firms, some in association with power networks. Each group will develop its design with full government co-operation. Costs will be borne mainly by AEC, although in a few cases industry agrees to foot a large share of the bills and take most of the risks.

Since the original law still stood on the books when the plan was initiated, all work so far has been in closely guarded secrecy. In January, 1954, President Eisenhower asked Congress to liberalize the act and the Joint Committee immediately began work on a new bill for the purpose. As this chapter is written committee hearings on it are complete and the new law is a virtual certainty. When it is enacted the future of atomic power will truly belong to the people.*

* The liberalized Atomic Energy Act was passed on August 30, 1954 and quickly signed by the President. As this book goes to press, secrecy in peaceful atomic work has already been much relaxed.

5. Big Experiments

• • • • • • • •

THE AMERICAN people now stand at the beginning of the age of atomic power. The first of the five projects is well under way. It is a full-sized plant, to be built by the Westinghouse Electric Corp., and operated by the Duquesne Light and Power Co., of Pittsburgh. It will produce 60,000 kilowatts of electric energy—enough for a city of 100,000 people—and will be located at Shippingport, Pa. The President himself broke ground for the project on September 6, 1954.

A conventional plant of this capacity would use up 40 million pounds of coal a month. But a six-year-old child could lift the amount of uranium fuel the new plant will use in that time.

It is hard for us on the outside to grasp the extraordinary complications of this major adventure in science and engineering. It will be pioneering in nearly every detail, so far as the atomic "boiler" is concerned, and pioneering at an enormously accelerated rate. Sixty years were required to bring the diesel engine from the laboratory to the railroads. The atomic engine will have made the same journey in a dozen. Even this is relatively slow by today's atomic standards. We built the bomb from a standing start in three years, and thus set a new pace which is becoming a part of the fabric of American progress.

The atom is impatient of delay.

It is not a wild prediction to say that the Shippingport plant will work virtually as the designers expect. But it is highly "chancy" for all that. It will work mainly in the sense that the power expected will be delivered. Beyond that anything may happen.

By "anything" I mean, for instance, that no one can predict how reliable the great machine will be. The atomic reactor is a highly intricate device, built to operate in a critical range of temperatures and pressures. Some of the metals in it will be newcomers to civilian use and will be driven close to their sup-

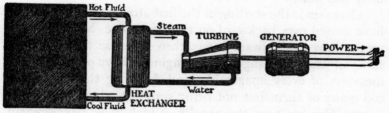

posed limits of strength and as hot as they can safely stand. Part of the structure will be under constant bombardment by radioactivity and neutrons in enormous concentration, and will perform in a closed container which nobody can enter, surrounded by many tons of concrete walls.

The plant will be engineered and supervised by experts who have had experience with atomic piles, but it will be full of innovations nevertheless and will be operated by technicians and artisans who are learning as they go. If an emergency arises no conventional procedure will be there to fall back on; remedies will have to be invented on the spot.

By the time this plant is in service the AEC and its contractors will have rounded out some 16 years of experience with smaller apparatus of the same kind, and most of the wrinkles of operation will be known or anticipated, at small scale. The full-sized machine, however, is sure to pose outsize problems, not new in themselves, but unfamiliar because of their huge dimensions.

Outsiders may wonder if this isn't a dangerous experiment, undertaken in the midst of a densely populated area. Actually, it is not. We shall see later that an atomic reactor is not a bomb, and cannot possibly explode; it can only melt and ruin itself within its own four walls. Such a catastrophe has happened only once in half a hundred reactors in 13 years, and nobody was hurt.

Ever since the starting of the first atomic pile the pioneers have leaned over backward on the safety side. Most elaborate precautions have always been taken. Because they were not sure just what the dangers were, engineers have provided safety measures of every imaginable kind, knowing that there were too many of them but not being sure just which were superfluous. This has been the penalty of high-speed development. A slower pace would have solved the safety problems in the laboratory and cost us many years of delay.

One of the fascinations of working with the atom is to protect yourself too well and then drop off, one by one, the safeguards that have proved unnecessary, watching efficiency improve and costs and complications ease away. This, indeed, is one of the main reasons for building this first experimental plant. It is a "learner," the Model T of the new art, and the pioneers are like boys in their eagerness to find out how many of their predictions will come true and where they have gone off the track. The game is played, of course, on a fearfully technical level, but it is a game all the same. It is the rarest kind of excitement to be living through a major experiment in changing civilization in five years, that in preatomic times might have taken a generation.

A tantalizing feature of the job is that hundreds of changes will be made as the work progresses. With a score of government and industrial laboratories working on new materials and processes, the project must be kept elastic all the way through. Almost every day plans will change; a new piping system, a new pump, a better material will come to light and heads will be put together to see how it can be substituted with the least dislocation of plans and at the smallest cost. This is the kind of experimenting that American pioneers always have dreamed about but rarely had a chance to try.

Learning as you go along, at full industrial scale, is a fantastically expensive proposition, becoming even more so if the time is short. It could not be done without government participation. But Congress feels that the people are ready to buy their way into the atomic age in a hurry and so the game is on. There is not the slightest danger that the people are giving away their atomic birthright so that private individuals can make a fortune. Nobody will make a profit for a long time. Contrary to popular belief the great majority of large contractors who built the bomb plants did so at cost plus a small fee—often as little as $1 a year.

This is the situation today and will be tomorrow, as atomic power takes the place of the bombs. American enterprise is not hogging the atom. As Gordon Dean of the AEC has said, it is going along through a worthy combination of motives: patriotism and the desire to learn the art for the general good of the country, including themselves.

The four other projects which the Atomic Energy Commission has decided to run concurrently with this first large plant are to be small by comparison. They are experiments, too, but will purposely be kept at the pilot-plant level to test variations in the basic principle. Each one will be farmed out to a contractor and paid for on a joint basis, and each will be watched by the AEC and the Joint Committee with an eagle eye. Not a week will pass, probably, but reports of progress will fly back and forth, conferences will be held, debates and wrangles and arguments carried on. Out of all this will be forged the firm foundation that will give the United States the lead in peaceful atomic energy that President Eisenhower has asked for.

This, then, will be the first inning in the great new game of atomic power. Uncertainty, compromise, discovery, the balancing of one advantage against another, the quick retirement from a path that has suddenly turned into a blind alley, and the setting out upon a fresh trail. It is emphatically the way America ought to do things, but except in dire war emergency never quite has.

Dr. Walter H. Zinn, director of the AEC's Argonne Laboratory in Chicago, recently reported an experiment which is typical of the spirit of the vast project. Argonne is the nation's headquarters for atomic reactor design and Dr. Zinn is one of the world's leading authorities on the subject.

The experiment was made to find out what would happen if an atomic power plant "ran away," completely out of control. Everybody wanted to know how safe such plants were going to be—whether the vast "exclusion areas" typical of the great bomb plants of Oak Ridge and Hanford would be needed for civilian power. If they were, the atom would be under a very serious handicap indeed.

The experiment (said Dr. Zinn) consisted of setting up and operating a nuclear reactor and then imposing conditions on the reactor which would make it "run away." This means that the power of the machine was caused to rise precipitously and was allowed to continue to rise indefinitely. Under such conditions it had been assumed in the past that the core of the reactor would melt and that this would permit the escape of radioactive fission products. (Such an accident actually happened at Chalk River in Canada. It will be described later.)

It is this particular assumed circumstance which has governed decisions concerning locations of nuclear reactors and which has required an uninhabited, restricted area surrounding them of an acreage which is determined by the power of the operation.

The experiment showed that power excursions of very large magnitude and which took place quite rapidly did not produce melting of the fuel and no radioactive contamination of the surroundings whatsoever resulted. The favorable effects observed were anticipated and are due to the particular design of the reactor, which is so arranged that the formation of steam quenches the nuclear reaction. In experiments in which the power was allowed to rise to many thousand watts in a fraction of a second, the steam process nevertheless quenched the nuclear reaction completely long before a dangerous temperature was induced.

We shall see further on how steam can quench the nuclear "fire." The stranger might say at once, Very well, here is your solution to safety in atomic power. It may not be at all. It may cost too much, or it may seriously lower efficiency, or be too complicated in giant sizes. But it does typify the vigorous search that is going on for making the exploding atom a decent member of the community.

6. Whence Atomic Power?

· · · · · · · · · · · ·

WHEN THE heart of an atom splits in the mysterious dissolution called fission, its fragments fly out with gigantic energy, at speeds of some 6,000 miles a second. When they hit other atoms of fuel, or the walls of the container or the "moderator" which surrounds it, they set billions of additional atoms into violent motion, which is another name for heat. As the fission chain reaction goes on, every innocent bystander atom is involved and the whole core of the machine becomes very hot. Remove this heat by circulating a fluid through the device and you get power that you can use.

If the reactor is made very compact and contains extremely pure specialized fuel *and is without control*, the chain reaction increases wildly, in a fraction of a millionth of a second, and you get a bomb. Temperatures at the instant of explosion have been estimated at some 50 million degrees.

This was atomic energy as science finally achieved it in the war. Given plutonium or the specially separated uranium-235, and extreme accuracy in every part, and the bomb was relatively simple. The only control needed was a trigger which would not go off till the bomb was hovering over its target.

The controlled atomic fission that produces power, kilowatt by kilowatt at everyday temperatures, is a far more difficult and cumbersome achievement. The crux of the problem is the fission chain reaction itself—a highly critical affair, with a tendency to go like mad or not at all. There is no theoretical limit to the power rate at which the reaction can proceed; the limit must be imposed by man and made to work without fail.

The actual discovery of uranium fission in 1938 is credited to the German scientists, Hahn, Strassmann, Meitner and Frisch, in Berlin. It was not truly a discovery but the final checking up in a drama of pioneering which began in 1919. In that year Sir Ernest Rutherford in England succeeded in transmuting a few atoms of nitrogen into oxygen by bombardment with the rays from radium. Rutherford understood that this alchemy was not concerned with the chemistry of whole molecules, but with the heart or nucleus of the tiny single atom itself.

At about the time of Rutherford's work the great Danish physicist, Niels Bohr, had established a picture of the atom which seemed to fit the known facts. He conceived of it as a tiny solar system with a central "sun" (the nucleus) surrounded by a cloud of "planets" (electrons). Like our own solar system, the body of the atom is mostly space, traversed by mysterious forces which hold the assembly together with gigantic bonds.

All this had been discussed and debated over the scientific world for years, when Rutherford demonstrated that the atom's nucleus was itself a little world of particles that might be altered to change one element in nature into another. Immediately investigators everywhere set themselves to probe the nucleus, hoping to find out what existed inside and what superlative forces held its parts together in defiance of every known disrupting force. To do this, experiments were devised to knock the nucleus apart by bombarding it with various atomic particles that were available. The only missiles at hand then were the proton, or hydrogen nucleus, and the alpha particle, or helium nucleus, the latter easily obtained from radium.

There was a serious difficulty, however. All atomic nuclei carry heavy electrical charges; so do protons and alphas. All of them are positive in sign and so repel each other violently. In those early days there were no huge machines such as cyclotrons and synchrotrons to seize the particles and hurl them with colossal energies at atomic targets. The relatively feeble forces of natural radium were not enough to drive a particle into a nucleus against the enormous push of repulsion. Thus, most of the shots expended their energies by knocking off electrons in the remote outer spaces of the atoms. Not one direct hit in a million shots could be made.

The problem was supremely difficult because the atom is so small while the nucleus is still smaller. It takes 100 million whole atoms side by side to make an inch. There are 70 thousand billion billion of them in a single ounce of uranium, and uranium is the largest and heaviest atom in nature.

The actual diameter of an atom is entirely beyond conception, it is so tiny. Yet its heart is 10,000 times smaller, though it contains 99.9 per cent of the total mass. Analogies that effectively visualize this minute world in human terms are hard to find. An atomic pioneer, Dr. John R. Dunning of Columbia, suggests a good one. If the atom is imagined to be as big as a large auditorium the nucleus would correspond in size to something like a pea suspended in the center.

An atomic scientist to the same scale, occupying a large fraction of the heavens, would be shooting other peas at it from the neighborhood of the stars, and all the while totally unable to see either target or missile with an eye as big as the solar system. (This second part of the analogy is mine, not Dunning's).

So atom-smashing is quite a trick.

Whence Atomic Power?

During the '20s and early '30s science concentrated on inventing guns that would do this atomic shooting job with ever-increasing energy, and with streams of bullets so numerous that hits were bound to be made. The first great success was scored by Dr. Ernest O. Lawrence, with the building of the cyclotron at the University of California in 1932. Here at last was the start of a line of disintegrators that today can hurl particles with the fantastic energy of billions of electron volts. But even today these machines cannot tear apart uranium atoms enough to gain useful atomic power. These so-called "accelerators" use far more energy to break down an atom than is given up in the smash. It required the discovery of the strange and unsuspected neutron particle by Sir James Chadwick in England in 1932, to do it.

By incredibly painstaking research Chadwick established that there must be another basic particle beside the proton and the electron in the atomic family. Eventually he identified it by its peculiar tracks across his photographic plates. It had about the same weight as the proton but possessed an astounding property that it shared with no other particle: it was entirely devoid of electric charge. Because of this peculiarly neutral electrical personality, Chadwick named it the neutron, and received the Nobel prize for its discovery.

The scientific world seized upon the neutron with great excitement. A whole new vista of atom-smashing had opened up. Neutrons could be obtained by knocking them out of finely powdered beryllium with the rays from radium. The speed with which they flew out was tremendous—some 40,000 miles per second. This was more than enough for bombarding a target of any desired substance. In fact, it was soon discovered that neutrons moving lazily at slow speeds worked even better. Being unaffected by the electric repulsion of the atom's nucleus they were easily absorbed by such atoms. "Slow" neutrons could be obtained by bouncing "fast" ones around in a "moderator" made of some light material till they lost most of their energy.

Successful atom-smashing with them was something like drifting a barge filled with high explosive into the midst of a fleet at anchor at night.

Atomically speaking, a typical ten-gram source of neutrons did not produce very many of the particles—only about ten million per second. But since the score of hits on a target was far higher than with charged particles, atom-smashing had reached an entirely new level of efficiency.

With the coming of the neutron physicists began to understand the puzzling matter of atomic weights. At that time there were 92 separate and distinct elements. These fitted step by step, according to their weights, into a table of elements devised by the Russian, Mendelyeef, in 1869. It had been supposed that the mass of each atom nucleus was made up of the sum of the masses of the protons in it. But each proton contributed one unit of electric charge to the nucleus and in all cases except hydrogen there were not enough charges to account for the known weights. Now it was apparent that the excess atomic weight was accounted for by neutrons in the nucleus. *Almost* accounted for, that is. There was still some small departure from predicted figures.

In brilliant work back in 1910 the Englishman, Frederick Soddy, had shown that the element lead could have several different atomic weights, although all lead behaved the same chemically. He chose the word "isotope" to denote these various species of the element and predicted that other substances would show a similar variety. It was a coined word based on the Greek denoting "the same place"—in the atomic table.

Now, with the neutron in the picture, it could be seen that the isotopes of an element differed from one another by the number of neutrons they possessed. The small discrepancies in atomic weight explained themselves as due to the varying proportions of the isotopes in any given sample of an element.

But there was a new mystery: What were the staggering forces that allowed the neutrons to bind an atomic nucleus together in spite of the tremendous repulsion between the associated protons?

Immediately the question occupied researchers everywhere. To answer it they launched into intensive studies of the isotopes. Today a thousand or more are known and well understood. But the nature of the binding forces is a continuing mystery.

In some elements there have proved to be many isotopic variations, in others only a few. Most hydrogen has no neutrons at all (though "heavy" hydrogen has one and tritium, two). As you go on up through the scale of the elements you find that, in general, there are more neutrons in an atomic nucleus than there are protons. Among the very heavy elements the preponderance of neutrons is enough to make the atom clumsy and unstable. From polonium to uranium all these elements are radioactive—that is, they disintegrate spontaneously, throwing off small particles (as radium does) and so gradually descending through the weight scale. Through successive generations they produce "daughter" elements of greater or lesser stability till they all end up as three solidly stable isotopes of lead.

Radioactivity in uranium had been discovered by Henri Becquerel in Paris in 1896. Inspired by him the Curies isolated polonium and radium two years later. Soddy and Rutherford, as young instructors at McGill University in Montreal, soon predicted the basic fact that the atom could produce gigantic energy if once torn apart. But no one knew the route to such a disintegration till the neutron's function was understood. Now it was evident that too large a nucleus, with too many neutrons in it, is out of balance, held together for a certain average length of time, then shuddering and throwing off an elemental article such as an alpha, a beta (electron) or a gamma ray—or a combination of them.

The average *rate* of this decay is always the same for a particular isotope of a radioactive element, so that it is possible to predict just how long it will take any given sample of the element to change into its daughter element. From this comes the concept of the *half-life* of the element, measured in seconds, days, years or centuries. In that time half of all the atoms in a sample will undergo change. This is a factor we shall meet with constantly in considering atomic energy and its uses.

A natural question that followed on an understanding of neutrons and isotopes was: what will an atom nucleus do if it is forcibly loaded with more neutrons than it can comfortably contain? Here began the marvelous era of the radioisotopes, the fantastic age of man-made atoms which nature cannot make, and of the wholesale transmutation of one element into another toward a goal that centuries of alchemists could not reach.

What you produce by attaching an extra neutron to an atom's nucleus is a new isotope of the same element, usually in a state of slight atomic indigestion. Depending on how unstable the new combination is, the atom will assume a state of radioactivity, sending out one or more small particles which will alter its electric charge and turn it into an atom of some near-by element in the scale.

If these "rays" come out at high speed (that is, high energy) you have an event of considerable magnitude, by atomic standards, but it is never powerful enough to be classed as usable energy. Nor does the excited atom usually manage to rid itself of the offending neutron. This seems sure to remain at the expense of other members of the nuclear family.

At least, this was the belief during the 1930's, when excitement over the neutron ran high. But at this point scientists here and there began to speculate on the possibilities of obtaining practical atomic energy by attacking great numbers of atoms all at once with armies of neutrons. As early as 1935 they predicted that some element might be found that a neutron could split apart in a major explosion, spilling out an important fraction of the total binding energy that had held it together. Dr. Dunning was one who believed this possible; the Austrian researcher, Frau Noddack, was another. They did not get much consideration at the time.

"This kind of talk," says Dunning, "was considered ridiculous, foolish, or at least visionary in most circles. . . . It is perhaps interesting to note that many who condemned this reasoning ten or fifteen years ago are talking most vigorously about atomic energy today." *

The point was that, in 1935, nobody except these few saw any hope at all of producing billions of free neutrons ready to go to work on equal billions of target atoms. The possibility that exploding atoms would throw out these armies themselves was not appreciated.

During 1934 Enrico Fermi and his colleagues at the University of Rome tried bombarding uranium with neutrons from the usual radium-beryllium source. The results, though mild, were completely mystifying. Occasionally large spurts of unexplained energy accompanied the fragments that burst out of the reaction. The Italian group thought that they had discovered a new element, perhaps No. 93. It was then that Frau Noddack remarked that she thought the chemical analysis of

---

* The Future of Atomic Energy, by J. R. Dunning, *American Scientist,* Jan., 1950.

the reaction products hadn't been careful enough, and that these fragments might turn out to be familiar elements farther down the atomic scale. She did not make any impression, for Hahn's group in Berlin (Hahn was a chemist) was soon proving the same thing that Fermi had proved: uranium bombardment produced at least two new elements, possibly Nos. 93 and 97.

In Paris Irene Curie also found fault with the thoroughness of the chemical analysis. So Hahn and his co-workers began again, carrying out a most delicate chemical separation of the reaction products. It was in December, 1938, that they found, to their consternation, minute traces of barium when uranium was hit by neutrons. What Lise Meitner called the "fission" of uranium had taken place.

This seemed to show that uranium fission produced, at least occasionally, large fragments instead of the usual little ones, and that these accounted for the great energy of the explosion.

It was Meitner who, fleeing the Nazis and taking her data with her, worked out the mathematics of the discovery in consultation with Niels Bohr in Denmark. A brand new kind of atom-smashing had been done. This was not a case of chipping off little pieces of an atom, but of blowing it wide apart. A uranium nucleus hit by a neutron was rent asunder cleanly, and the two fragments were driven outward by the huge internal forces of repulsion.

Still there was no promise of atomic energy in quantity, for a suitable rich source of free neutrons was not available, unless it should be in the uranium atoms themselves.

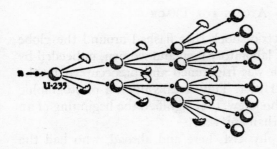

7. Atomic Energy Is Born

• • • • • • • • • • •

NIELS BOHR came to America in mid-January, 1939, to lecture at Princeton. Here and at Columbia he immediately discussed the world-shaking idea of uranium fission with his many friends. They already knew about it, of course, but Bohr, as the world's foremost theoretical physicist, gave authenticity and urgency to the account. Immediately, scientists at Columbia began duplicating the Berlin experiments.

"You can appreciate our excitement," wrote Dunning, who was a leading investigator at Columbia, "when we first saw this enormous release of energy . . . of 200 million electron volts. This is about 50,000 times the energy from burning a single atom of carbon in coal with oxygen." *

At Princeton Bohr and his former pupil, John A. Wheeler, made computations that showed that the rare isotope, uranium-235, was responsible for fission. Far more abundant U-238, they decided, did not contribute.

These historic computations, scrawled on a little blackboard in Wheeler's laboratory, are still there—or were, at any rate, the last time I visited him.

The state of excitement during the spring of 1939 is hard

* The Future of Atomic Energy, by J. R. Dunning, *American Scientist*, Jan., 1950.

to describe—an electric shock that flashed around the globe among thousands of laboratory men and women, unheeded by the lay world, which was frightened and preoccupied by the growing menace of Hitler. Tiny streaks upon a photographic plate, yet to those who knew, they signified the beginning of an era more important than any war.

Literally every physicist, here and abroad, who had the equipment to do it, repeated the fission experiment, using almost invisible samples of uranium. During that year more than 100 technical papers were published, confirming the discovery.

In the United States, meetings and conferences were held in rapid succession. At one of them Fermi, fresh from work he had been doing at Columbia, electrified his audience by calmly announcing that he thought a fission "chain reaction" was possible. It was probably true, he said, that the breakup of one uranium atom would yield *new* neutrons as well as tremendous energy. Some of these neutrons could go on to cause further fissions, which in turn would release still more neutrons. Thus, a reaction in uranium, started by a single neutron from outside, might be self-perpetuating, might even grow larger and larger through successive generations. You would then have atomic energy in quantity.

The whole thing would depend, said Fermi, on just how many fresh neutrons were produced by each exploding uranium atom. If, on the average, it should be only one, a chain reaction could theoretically just sustain itself, but in practice would not because some neutrons were bound to get lost, while some uranium atoms would not explode.

But if the neutron gain with each fission were two or more, enough, say, so that two made good with each generation, this staggering condition would result:

The first (stray) neutron causes one fission—
    which causes two more fissions—

which cause four more fissions—
which cause eight more fissions—

. . . . . .

By the 10th generation there would be 1024 new fissions
  By the 20th generation, over a million
    By the 60th generation, over a billion billion
      And by the 100th generation, somewhere around a
      thousand billion billion billion!

And, Fermi added quietly, since *all this* could happen easily within a millionth of a second, you could have a gigantic explosion of energy, virtually instantaneously.

The galaxy of leading physicists who heard this fantastic prediction realized that they were face to face with a major crisis in the history of science. Nature was about to present the world with the incredible power of atomic energy, or she was not. That single fact of the number of free neutrons per fission would decide. Two or more per fission, yes. Less than two, no.

Many a hand shook as its owner left the hall that day.

The fundamental fact to be discovered was this figure of neutrons per fission. But first they must know which of the two principal isotopes of uranium was doing the splitting. Were Bohr and Wheeler right in their calculations that showed it to be only the isotope of atomic weight 235? If so, there was a hard road ahead, for U-235 is extremely rare—139 times as rare as the common isotope U-238. In any lump of natural uranium only about $\frac{7}{10}$ of one per cent. Furthermore, the two atomic weights were so nearly equal that separation might be impossible, certainly next to impossible on anything but a laboratory scale.

Practically no researcher had the equipment or the specialized knowledge to tackle this nearly impossible separation problem. But there was one—A. O. Nier—who agreed to try. It took him one full year of steady work with his complicated mass spectrograph to produce one one-hundred-millionth of a gram of concentrated U-235.

On March 2, 1940, this invisible embryo of the atomic age was placed with utmost care in the neutron beam of the cyclotron at Columbia, while the staff stood tensely waiting for the moment when they could develop and examine the photographic plate associated with the experiment.

Observation, measurement, computation which lasted for days. Then came the answer: there was no doubt about it, uranium-235 was responsible.

The political crisis was galloping across Europe like a forest fire. Not many months before, Hitler had burst into Poland. Now, in the spring of 1940, the flames were crackling closer and closer to England and France. News had come by grapevine that the Kaiser Wilhelm Institute in Berlin, where fission had first been announced, had set aside a whole department for the study of uranium. No informed scientist in America doubted that a German uranium bomb was to be attempted.

There was no time to be lost on this side. The basic fact of the neutron production of fission must be determined at once, so that an American version of the bomb could be begun.

Nuclear physicists, augmented by many who were fleeing the rising storm abroad, swiftly got together and clamped down their own voluntary censorship. The President was informed that a bomb was possible. Six thousand dollars of Navy funds were allocated to preliminary studies. The most terrible arms race in history had begun.

The neutrons-per-fission factor, k, was soon determined. Not a handful of men in America knew what it was, but the fact that work on uranium suddenly burgeoned, was proof that it was big enough to fulfill the conditions that Fermi had laid down.

It was not until 1952 that the value of k was actually announced. Nature had played into our hands generously. Not 1, not 2, but more than 2.5 had proved to be the neutron factor— ample to permit a chain reaction to build up in a suitable environment at enormous speed.

If it had been only 2, said Dunning succinctly, one could practically have forgotten about an atomic age. With a value of 3, it would have made many phases of nuclear engineering "almost easy." As it was, staggering problems were ahead for the bomb, problems that, until the very day of the first detonation, no one was quite sure could be solved.

But no American scientist was afraid to try. Under the able direction of Dr. Vannevar Bush, director of the new Office of Scientific Research and Development, the ultrasecret bomb project was now co-ordinated. The first thing was to build an actual machine to prove that the chain reaction would work. Fortunately, it would not be necessary to construct a bomb at the start. A carefully controlled chain reaction would demonstrate the principle.

The whole thing depended upon neutron economy—that is, how to prevent the fission neutrons from wandering away, from being absorbed by impurities in the structure or by uranium atoms that failed to "fiss." Preliminary design of the pile worked out at about twelve tons of the purest possible natural uranium, plus a large quantity of equally pure graphite to "moderate" the flying neutrons, keep them in the pile and slow them down to the best speed for causing fission.

The first real problem was to find enough uranium and learn to remove its impurities. This was a staggering job. Nobody had ever wanted uranium in tons before. Little more than a few pounds was available in any laboratory at the time. The requirement seemed hopeless. Every known source in this country and abroad was combed. Gradually the stream of metal began to pour in.

Next came purification and reduction to the final metal bricks which had been specified, a story too complicated to detail here. Uranium looks rather like stainless steel but is much heavier. An ordinary-sized brick might weigh close to 100 pounds.

One by one the shining blocks of the strange new metal were turned out and sent to Chicago, where scientists under Dr. Arthur Compton at the University of Chicago built them and the similar graphite bricks into a peculiar beehive-shaped struc-

ture as fast as they arrived. This lattice-formed pile of fuel and moderator was the simplest construction possible. It has turned out to be one of the best, and many atomic piles like it have since been built.

The marvel of it was that, except for a few key people, no one knew what was going on in Chicago. Even the thousands of mining and refining and transportation people along the way did not know. The experiment was to be the best-kept secret America had ever had.

The site chosen for this first experiment was a cavernous squash court under the west stands of the Stagg Field stadium, in the middle of Chicago. It was named the Metallurgical Laboratory and was out of bounds to all but the few who moved in and out with all the innocence they could assume.

Though these men were trying to develop a source of energy millions of times greater than anything the world had ever seen, they were not alarmed at the prospect that they might blow a gaping hole in the city of Chicago. They knew well enough that the real danger lay in not being able to conserve enough neutrons within the pile to cause any reaction at all. Till the last few days of the building of the pile, success or failure remained in the balance.

But on December 2, 1942, all doubts came to an end. Long before the last few hundred pounds of fuel and moderator had been put in place, instruments announced that the neutron atmosphere inside the pile was rapidly thickening. Unexpectedly on that day "criticality" was reached. Enough neutrons were circulating to start the chain reaction in the atoms of uranium-235 embedded in the larger mass of U-238. Theory had moved into practice sooner than computation had predicted.

Much dramatic fiction has been written of this historic moment. We see a little knot of world-famous scientists standing tense and breathless as one of the younger men, with shaking hand, inches back the control rods and coaxes the chain reaction to begin. Except for the hysterical chattering of neutron counters there is no sound, as the invisible atomic particles surge into life behind massive concrete walls. You could hear an atom drop; no one dares even to think.

Rows of tiny neon lights skip like fairy fire across the faces of the instrument boards. Unbearably tense, the men who created this Frankenstein stand riveted in their tracks, wondering if, at the next moment, they will be face to face with eternity.

43

Then, deliberately, the expert at the console shoves the control rods home. The blinking and the chattering die down. The grand experiment is over. The chain reaction is a fact! And it can be stopped! Silently perspiring men shake hands and bow their heads. . . .

Actually, nothing of the kind took place at Stagg Field that day. Constant measurements and calculations during the months while the pile was being built showed when and how the reaction would begin. This was far too important an experiment to permit diversion of emotions into bug-eyed wonder or fear. American science was waiting for vital data on which the whole bomb project would be built. Day by day new information was emerging, to be flashed to other laboratories and to the desks of war executives whose future plans depended upon it.

Week after week, as the blocks of fuel and graphite were fitted into the lattice, the neutron count increased. Several times modifications in the shape of the structure were made, as it became apparent how best to conserve the little particles. And when at last the critical point was reached and it came time to man the controls, it was known beyond any doubt that the reaction could be held to any level desired. This was well. For there was no shielding at all.

For a few minutes that December day the pile was allowed to run and the level of power permitted was two watts—enough to light a flashlight and no more.

8. The Bomb Works
• • • • • • • • •

WHEN URANIUM is mined and refined the "natural" metal contains 139 parts of the 238 isotope to one of the 235. The meaning of the last two figures is simple: in U-238 there are 92 protons and 146 neutrons, while in U-235 there are the same 92 protons but only 143 neutrons. The number of protons remains constant for all isotopes of an element. This "atomic number," or electric charge, is the identifying characteristic of the element.

Both isotopes of uranium are radioactive but their half-lives are very long. U-238 loses half its atoms to thorium in four billion years; U-235 decays in similar fashion in 700 million. Nature gave us a break in this. If either or both of these isotopes had had half-lives even down in the millions of years the supply of it would have disappeared and there would be no atomic age. As it is, U-235 has had time to become very scarce since the beginning of the universe.

The scientists who undertook to make the first uranium bomb well understood the problem posed by the scarcity of U-235, the fissionable isotope. It would be necessary to separate out many pounds of U-235 from large quantities of the commoner material. This separation promised to be the largest ordnance operation ever undertaken anywhere. But it had to be done because a reaction of real explosive violence could not be obtained if U-238 were present to steal away a lot of the neutrons. A slow power reaction had been obtained at Chicago, using the thinly dispersed U-235 in 12 tons of ordinary metal. For the bomb, pure 235 would be necessary.

Assuming that a piece of the rare material about the size of a baseball was the objective of the scientists for each bomb (the actual figure is still a deep secret), a good many hundred pounds of it would have to be refined, *an atom at a time.* The result was the building of immense plants at Oak Ridge, Tennessee, using two different methods of separation, working day and night for more than two years, and costing the country roughly a billion dollars. Electric power sufficient to supply all of New York City was needed to drive thousands of pumps, huge magnets and other equipment.

One of the most important pieces of data to come from Chicago was a fact long suspected by the physicists: that when an atom of the common U-238 is hit by a neutron a transmutation takes place, yielding a new man-made element—No. 93. This may have been what confused Fermi nine years before. The Stagg Field pile had produced barely enough of the new element for accurate identification. But it had revealed one more favor which nature intended to do for man.

The new element, called neptunium, had a half-life of only a few days, changing itself spontaneously into still another new

46

element, No. 94. Here was the payoff. Plutonium, the second daughter of U-238, turned out to be fissionable in the same way as U-235, by neutrons. Even better, it gave off *three* neutrons, on the average, with each event. By some lucky chance, Pu-239 (short for plutonium) possessed a half-life of 24,000 years, hence could be made in a slow-burning atomic pile and stored as bomb fuel.

The Chicago pile did not generate enough plutonium even for study by microchemical methods. However, the cyclotrons at Berkeley and at the University of St. Louis were quickly put to work making more by a little different method. Thus, during 1943, an amount was made equal to the weight of one perforation on a postage stamp. Upon this infinitesimal quantity enough experiments were performed to justify the expenditure of another billion dollars for the gigantic plutonium atomic piles at Hanford, Washington. So, while Oak Ridge raced against time to separate out tangible quantities of fissionable uranium, Hanford set to work just as furiously to create plutonium by the pound.

Never before have science and engineering founded a major industry upon the behavior of quantities of material too small to see. It was a wild gamble; no sane man would have done it in peacetime. But it was the willingness to take that fantastic chance that has brought atomic energy in our lifetime.

By mid-'43 the Army had taken over, under the grim but able leadership of Maj. Gen. Leslie R. Groves. On top priority and in bottomless secrecy the vast project moved ahead, solving problems in chemistry, physics, metallurgy, engineering and human protection as it went. Called, in the stiff nomenclature of the military, the Manhattan Engineer District, these thousands of specialists rode roughshod over every obstacle, telling no one, not even Congress, what the millions they demanded were for.

Insiders knew by this time that a bomb could be made. But could it be turned out in time? We did not know then that atomic science in Germany had bogged down; that Hitler had been told that an atomic bomb was impossible.

The two methods of separation of the uranium isotopes were extremely complicated, critical and tedious, and will be described in more detail in a later section, since they form the basis of a more or less permanent manufacturing process that will probably be used in civilian atomic power. The method of producing plutonium followed the principle of the first atomic pile at Chicago. Enormous structures of natural uranium and graphite were built. When the control rods were pulled out, the U-235 set up its chain reaction and the neutrons not needed to keep it going were free to join with U-238 atoms to make neptunium and hence plutonium.

When several months had passed the aluminum cans in which the fuel was sealed were discharged by remote control into a great chemical plant, into which no human being could go because of the intense radioactivity. Here, the tiny amount of plutonium created was successfully dissolved out of its metallic birthplace, and stored. The remaining uranium was purified of the various other fission products—all extremely "hot" —then sealed in new aluminum cans and returned to the piles to make more plutonium. In the entire chemical cycle no living person ever touched or approached the materials. Everything was done by remote control from behind massive concrete walls.

By the spring of 1945 small but real quantities of the two bomb-making metals had come off the production lines at Oak Ridge and Hanford, and the first bombs were built. Everyone knows what happened next. But few know how incredibly small was the amount of the explosive material wrested from nature in two years. It has been published that the total fuel manufactured in that $2-billion secret venture would scarcely have filled a one-gallon bucket!

A fair estimate seems to be that the amount of matter which was annihilated in the bomb at Hiroshima, thereby annihilating the city and more than a hundred thousand of its people, was about the size of a ball bearing in a bicycle wheel.

The Hanford piles, of course, were not duplicates of the crude affair laid up by hand, brick by brick, at Chicago. They were intricate machines, vast conglomerations of pipes and ducts, automatic controls, meters, instruments and safety devices. They were, indeed, the first true prototypes of the machines that will some day furnish us with atomic power. For they were actually producing heat at the rate of hundreds of thousands of kilowatts. This heat was thrown away. Water, circulating through the piles, carried it off to be dumped into the Columbia River. Military production does not call for economy but only for speed and performance.

Here we can leave the bomb and trace from its beginning the modern atomic reactor. The bomb project had shown the way to refine atomic fuel and derive useful energy from it, and it had done this in a mere five years—an advance in engineering that at any other time would have taken fifty.

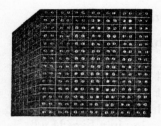

9. What Is a Reactor?

• • • • • • • • •

BY THE end of the war the basic elements of atomic power were well understood: first, sufficient fissionable material must be concentrated in a container to sustain a chain reaction. This must be surrounded by a moderator to slow down the neutrons and to prevent them from escaping. Next, there must be carefully positioned control rods, made of some "neutron stealer" like cadmium or boron. These must be hooked up to automatic power-measuring instruments so that just the right level of neutron flux will be maintained to hold any desired power level. The controls are vital and must act without human intervention if need be. No man's hand can move fast enough to interrupt the rise of power that could take place in a runaway reactor.

The next requirement is some kind of fluid, pumped through the heart of the reactor, in contact with the "burning" fuel, to carry away the intense heat generated by the flying fission fragments. This cooling medium can be water, air, helium, or a liquid metal. From the reactor it must be piped to a heat exchanger or boiler where it can give up its excess heat to water to make steam, thence returning to the reactor to pick up more.

The final essential is a heavy mass of concrete, steel or lead, built around the whole assembly to stop stray neutrons and radioactive fragments from flying out and endangering life.

A typical pile produces alpha, beta, gamma and neutron radiation thousands of times as powerful and dangerous as the emanations from radium.

The shield is a liability that cannot be avoided and must be heavy. For it is the total number of atoms in it that stop the radiations.

This is "all there is to it." Once steam has been generated outside the reactor, the atomic power plant becomes a conventional unit exactly like hundreds of coal-burning plants whose familiar stacks adorn every city. The turbines, generators, condensers, pumps and control devices are no different from those that many a high-school class has seen on its visit to the electric light company.

To be exact, the atomic reactor is only a part of the atomic power plant, and is nothing more than a new kind of furnace for turning out heat. It is a boiler which can replace the usual towering structure of firebed and tubes and flues and smokestacks with a compact machine of half the size (but considerably more cost). The atomic boiler has two very great advantages: the heat it generates is picked up directly by the contact of a circulating fluid with the "burning" fuel, and is carried to a highly efficient heat exchanger (or radiator) to make steam. The second advantage is more important. There is no practical limit to the intense temperatures of the atomic fires, and the higher the temperature the greater the efficiency and the smaller the apparatus. Thus, as the art moves on into the future greater and greater use will be made of atomic energy as we learn to fabricate materials that can work safely in an inferno of heat.

Today we have no metals that can hold their strength much beyond 1000 degrees F.* This is a sad limitation indeed,

---

* All the temperatures in this book are given in degrees Fahrenheit. Hereafter the F's will be omitted.

but in one way encouraging. For the metallurgist has only begun his work. Spurred on by the similar demand for high-temperature, high-strength materials imposed by jet propulsion and rockets, he is rapidly pushing his frontiers into the regions of incandescence. Every discovery he makes will be that much gain for atomic power.

Another serious limitation, temperature-wise, is posed by the cooling fluid. This is an entirely new field for engineering, for up to now water has given us practically everything we need as a heat-transfer medium. But water boils at such a low temperature that it will badly handicap an atomic reactor. Hence, as the art advances, better coolants that boil at much higher temperatures will have to be found. The first of these—a mixture of liquid sodium and potassium—has already appeared, and will actually be used in the second atomic submarine. But even sodium boils at about 1400 degrees, which is still "cool" from the atom's point of view. An important line of research today is aimed at finding cooling fluids that can do their work at thousands of degrees. If they are ever found we might have an atomic power plant no bigger than a piano.

There are other disadvantages in the atomic furnace, though they are likely to be temporary. One is that the fuel—uranium—is still very expensive in the very high purity that must be used. A second, and worse, trouble is that the fuel that makes power also makes bombs. No one knows whether the military will ever release control of fission fuel—certainly it won't for the present.

A third and perhaps the most embarrassing difficulty is the problem of disposing of the atomic "ashes" left behind in the reactor fuel by the fission process. The flying fragments which produce the heat inside a pile are lighter elements such as barium and xenon, intensely radioactive. Some have half-lives of hundreds or thousands of years. Their removal and storage out of reach of humanity has been a major problem at Hanford. They cannot be left in the fuel any more than ashes can be left in a home furnace; soon they poison it.

At Hanford vast quantities of liquid solutions of these by-products have been buried deep in the ground in great tanks. Temporarily, that is an answer. But when the world is dotted with huge atomic power plants ashes will pour out of them by the hundreds of tons. Atomic experts of AEC believe that the

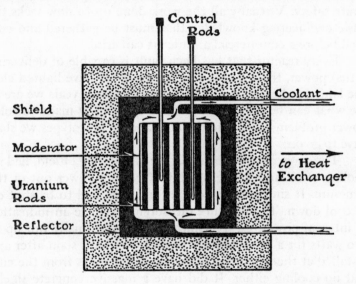

problem may become international, and that eventually vast areas of waste land will have to be given over to atomic ash-dumping and forever closed to human entry. Some slight help, as we shall see later, may be gained by using these waste products in industry and medicine, but it is doubtful if all possible uses can account for more than a small fraction of the unwelcome supply.

In the ten years since the war the AEC has steadily experimented with atomic machines, building one reactor after another to test out the amazing variety of designs that seem promising. There are more than 80 approaches to the problem. So far, the 30-odd reactors that have been built have all been research machines. Some are for testing neutron behavior, some for trying out new construction materials, some for manufacturing isotopes for medicine and industry. Others, such as the one mentioned by Dr. Zinn earlier, are designed to demonstrate safety. Virtually all the work done up to now seeks the basic engineering knowledge that must be gathered and codified before a commercial atomic art can arise.

Every reactor that has been built is capable of delivering actual power, though only one or two so far have lighted electric lamps or heated buildings. In the next five years we are to see what can be done with reactors specifically made to solve power problems. Here are the outstanding prototypes we shall have to go on:

The progenitor of them all, the pile at Stagg Field, had no cooling at all and hence no way of getting power out of the structure. It simply warmed itself up, then had to be shut off to cool down. Temperature measurements gave an indication of internal power. CP-1 (Chicago Pile) was finally run up to 200 watts for a short time. A second pile, built soon after and installed at the Argonne Laboratory a few miles from the city, had no cooling either. It did have a massive concrete shield, lacking in CP-1, and so could be run at a higher level without endangering the researchers with radiation. CP-2, still working, can attain 2000 watts.

Now we come to the first big one: the huge structure at Oak Ridge, built as a pilot plant for plutonium-making, and after the war turned into the world's first factory for radioisotopes. This reactor had to be cooled, because when its neutrons fly at full density to make the magic transmutations called isotopes, it generates 2000 *kilo*watts. This is a power output of respectable size. A 2000-kilowatt plant will care for a small town.

A blast of air cools this Oak Ridge pile, and is used because it offers the most inexpensive way to remove the heat. But air cooling would not do for commercial power production; air is one of the poorest mediums for carrying heat, if the heat is to be put to work. Engineers estimate that it costs 50,000 times as much to carry heat by air as it does to move it with liquid sodium. We use hot air circulation in houses because it is extremely simple and it is the warm air we want, anyway.

Next in succession come the giant reactors at Hanford, still following the original Chicago design of a lattice of uranium and graphite. But these structures are as big as a city office building, filled with hundreds of tons of uranium and thousands of tons of graphite moderator. Just how much power they turn out in making plutonium is a secret, though the production of only one pound of it per day gives 24,000,000 kilowatt-hours of heat.

Production figures at Hanford are withheld because they would give an enemy a good basis for guessing at our atomic strength. It is certain, however, that the power level runs into the hundreds of thousands of kilowatts. To get rid of it a very considerable part of the mighty Columbia River is diverted and pumped through the reactors. It comes out hot and slightly radioactive and is passed through delaying basins, where the radiation levels falls off to practically nothing. The water is then wasted into the river. The whole stream below the plant is said to be noticeably warmer.

The wasting of this enormous dividend in heat was a war necessity to save time and expense. General Electric, which runs the plant, has announced that a good deal of it will soon be used to warm the Hanford buildings. "In addition to being a milestone in the use of atomic energy," says G.E., "the new heat recovery process will pay for itself in about seven and a half years. After that it will mean an estimated saving of $57,000 a year to the AEC." A drop in the atomic bucket to the taxpayer, but a drop nevertheless.

Now we depart from the old original design and see several experimental atomic reactors taking shape. One is a small 300-kilowatt machine at Argonne, consisting of a tank of heavy water with uranium rods suspended in it. Heavy water, in which the hydrogen is the double-weight isotope called deuterium, is especially good as a slower-downer of neutrons. Better, in fact, than ordinary water or graphite. But it is expensive.

In the early days of the war atomic scientists believed that heavy water was essential to the chain reaction, and elaborate plans were laid to build distilleries to separate it from ordinary water (about 1 molecule in 5000 is heavy). The Germans had promptly built a heavy-water factory deep in a Norwegian fjord, where there was ample hydroelectric power for the complicated process. The Allies bombed it doggedly and finally a dramatic commando attack destroyed it in one of the decisive blows that ended Hitler's hopes for a bomb. Over here the hope of producing enough heavy water quickly enough, was abandoned and graphite used instead. The piles had to be much bigger, but graphite was available in any quantity.

You drink tens of thousands of heavy water molecules every day and never know the difference. Chemically it is identical to the ordinary kind. It was discovered by Dr. Harold Urey in 1931, and the scientific world waited expectantly when he drank a spoonful of it to see if it was harmful. Fortunately it wasn't. But that drink may have been worth $1000. Even today, heavy water costs $50 to $80 a pint and tons of it are needed in a single reactor. Nevertheless, it is coming into wide use again, since a fluid moderator has many advantages and cuts down the size of reactors.

Using fluid fuels was also an advance that came early. The first of these was the Los Alamos "water boiler," built in 1944. Instead of having uranium bricks or rods, it contained a "soup" of uranium sulfate in water, heavily enriched in U-235. The soup was contained in a small stainless-steel sphere and cooled by water flowing through a coil of pipe in the sphere. A step beyond this was the "homogeneous reactor," HRE, in which fluid fuel, coolant and moderator were all one liquid. We shall see as we go on that this has many advantages.

One more of the early reactors at Los Alamos should be mentioned. It was affectionately called "Clementine," because its code number was 49, suggesting the gold miners' famous song. Clementine worked on highly enriched fuel and was cooled by mercury—the first use of liquid metal. The advantage was that liquid metal boils at a much higher temperature than water and so can take away far more heat in each cubic inch. This was the beginning of the search for higher efficiency. Efficiency is the "indispensable man" in engineering.

Clementine was also a "fast" reactor. It used no moderator to slow the neutrons, which darted about at the speeds at which they were born in the chain reaction. The bomb works this way. Fast neutrons are satisfactory so long as the fuel is very rich in U-235.

In 1950 the AEC's Brookhaven Laboratory, far out on Long Island, launched the largest test reactor of all, a 30,000-kilowatt machine primarily built to produce a tremendous neutron storm. The neutrons were to be used for research in atomic physics and, on the side, to make radioisotopes of very high activity.

Here we are back to the old graphite-and-ordinary-uranium-block design, and with no attempt made to use the power. Thirty thousand kilowatts of heat, however, have to be dealt with. This is done by drawing huge quantities of air through the pile, monitoring it for radiation, and exhausting it up a tall stack. Brookhaven is now one of the two principal suppliers of radioactive materials, such as the famous cobalt-60 used in medicine.

Every one of these reactors, including the grandfather of them all, now at Argonne, is still in use, collecting invaluable information for the atomic future. And there are many more, and still others on paper, including the Materials Testing Reactor at Arco, Idaho, and a far-advanced machine just proposed at Brookhaven, in which a liquid alloy of uranium and bismuth is expected to solve many problems of cooling and waste disposal.

The Materials Testing Reactor (MTR) was one of the most essential research instruments in the entire project. It was put into use in 1952 to study the effects of neutrons and radioactivity upon fuel and structural materials of all kinds. A host of serious construction problems had already come up. The strongest materials from the old Age of Steel collapsed when riddled with neutrons. Even uranium itself could not keep its shape. It would be hopeless to try to build an atomic power industry through a bottleneck of physical limitations. It was as if the automobile industry had nothing but paper tires.

But MTR is breaking the bottleneck with the most intense flux of neutrons in the world. It has proved, for instance, that zirconium is the magic metal in the atomic field, indifferent to neutrons, resistant to intense heat. It has found that the rare metal hafnium is far superior as a neutron-grabber, hence as a control material.

Thus, the lesson we can learn in this first look at reactors is that we have yet only scratched the surface of an art as intricate and vast as the art of electronics. Study, and study only, will make progress possible. "The technological gap between producing a controlled chain reaction," says Dr. H. D. Smyth of AEC, "and using it as a large-scale power plant is comparable to the gap between the discovery of fire and the manufacture of a steam locomotive."

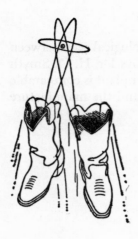

10. The Bootstrap Experiment
• • • • • • • • • • • •

FAR AND away the most promising atomic machine on the horizon now is a combination of several well-proved types known as the "breeder." Only a small supply of fissionable U-235 exists in nature. You can make fissionable plutonium in immense and expensive plants, and a little later on thorium metal will be transmuted into useful U-233. However, when an atom of any fissionable substance has exploded, it is gone—reduced to ashes—just as an atom of coal or gasoline is gone when it has been burned. Something has got to be done to make use of the relatively enormous supplies of nonfissionable uranium-238, or the atomic age will be over in its infancy.

The kernel of the secret lies in the Hanford giants, where huge quantities of heat are manufactured, *while making plutonium fuel*. During the war, the heat was thrown away, and the process was carried on at very low efficiency because there was no time to improve it. But soon after 1945 the scientists, notably Dr. Zinn, began to experiment with the idea that if you could increase the effectiveness of turning ordinary uranium into plutonium you might wind up with a process in which more plutonium atoms resulted than the number of U-235 atoms burned. In other words, you might "breed" fuel out of the inert U-238, *and get power while doing it.*

This sounded like magic: to shovel coal into a furnace, burn it, and then find you had more coal than when you started. Early press reports about breeding puzzled lay readers, who were given to think that the atomic age had at last turned up perpetual motion. Nothing of the kind was true. Breeding would merely mean that both kinds of uranium might be consumed, thus using the 99.1 per cent of the metal that had previously been unburnable.

A U-235 atom, when it splits, throws out an average of two and a half neutrons. If two of these should be captured by U-238 atoms, two atoms of plutonium would result. But the chain reaction would stop; at least one whole neutron is needed to split the next U-235. Only a small fraction of the neutrons produced plutonium in the wartime reactors because "neutron economy" was low. A lot were lost overboard, a lot more were stolen by the pile structure and by impurities. However, Dr. Zinn's pencil began to sketch designs in which the economy might be made much higher.

The trick was to save every single neutron for useful work. Frugality is an old game in power engineering, a game of compromise. Your car throws away three-quarters of its fuel because the engine is a poor converter of chemical into mechanical energy. It could be better if you cared to pay for it and never run it except on straight empty roads.

Once primed with a quantity of U-235 (or plutonium), the imagined breeder reactor would constantly convert U-238 into more plutonium than it started with, meantime producing heat for use as power. Nature had smiled once more on atomic science here. Plutonium fission gives off an average of *three* neutrons for each fission event. As the reaction goes on, more and more plutonium will result. In the end, perhaps after some years' use, one could perhaps stoke the atomic furnace with plain uranium and keep it going indefinitely. Zinn thought the same thing might be done with thorium.

A complete revolution in the young science of atomic power reached the horizon with this idea. With 139 times as much U-238 in the world as 235, supplies of atomic fuel would be greatly extended. And with the even more plentiful thorium to draw upon, a truly inexhaustible source of atomic power could be imagined.

Industrially, this was of utmost importance. It meant that nuclear energy might rise from a weak competitor of coal and oil to a giant that would actually drive fossil fuels out of the picture. It might extend cheap power sources by several thousand years. Atomic experts, especially Dr. Zinn, were very much excited indeed.

The actual design and construction of a breeder was far more difficult than dreaming about it, but work was begun at Argonne. A year or two ago the AEC announced that the first pilot model was complete and in service at Arco, Idaho. It worked. It was, indeed, connected to a 250-kilowatt generator and today supplies light and power for several laboratory buildings. It is the first atomic engine ever to furnish useful energy.

Dr. Zinn and his colleagues had done a remarkable job. The core, or reaction space of the machine, is no larger than a football, and contains a charge of pure U-235. It is surrounded by a metal jacket in which sodium and potassium metals circulate. This alloy is liquid at low temperatures. Outside the jacket comes a "blanket" of U-238, arranged in a cylindrical mass filled with holes for further circulation of the cooling fluid. The plutonium is made in the blanket. The whole thing is scarcely larger than a trunk.

However, the rest of the reactor is not so compact. Vital to the whole machine is a steady flow of the sodium-potassium mixture through the core and off to a heat exchanger. The liquid metal comes out of the center very hot—600 degrees or more—and very radioactive. Both sodium and potassium are explosive when they touch water. So, to guard against a bad accident, the designers have provided a double circulating system. The fluid that comes out of the core gives up its heat to a "secondary loop" of sodium-potassium, and the metal flowing here carries the heat to a second exchanger where steam is made for the turbine. Since one radioactive substance will not make another one radioactive, the second loop is merely hot, not "hot."

If ever a leak develops in the second loop where water comes close to liquid metal, thus causing an explosion, there will be no danger of spreading radioactive materials through the plant.

Essential to all this is a set of remarkable pumps without joints, seals or moving parts. These work by electromagnetic induction and were invented for the purpose at Argonne. The liquid to be pumped is supplied with a heavy current and acted upon by a powerful electromagnet. Obeying Faraday's dynamo principle, it moves continuously through the apparatus under the push of the magnetic field. Nothing moves except the fluid itself.

It is this kind of brilliant invention that has become an everyday affair with atomic energy. Since the beginning the atom has demanded man's top performance. In the future it will not only give him power but will force him to keep his brain razor-sharp.

No one believes at present that all future atomic plants

will be breeders. If they were, we might end up with an atomic army with nothing in it but generals. Probably only the largest power units need be of this type. Located with great care over the country they would form a strategic network of suppliers of fuel to many smaller stations and to medical and research reactors in all large cities. The government would probably obtain much of its bomb fuel from them. Such large breeders would no doubt be government-owned or controlled.

Recovering plutonium from a breeder is a complicated job. One doesn't simply open a door and take it out, box it and ship it. There is an expensive and dangerous chemical process to go through to separate the deadly "ashes" from the plutonium and the still unconsumed uranium. A big fraction of the cost at Hanford comes from operating this strange remote-controlled refinery where "hot chemistry" is conducted by mechanical robots under the scrutiny of television eyes and electronic muscles.

The Joint Committee hearings in 1953 brought out a lot of discussion on breeders that might be privately owned. Most power-company people shied away from assuming charge of plants whose output would have to be turned over to the government for distribution to other plants or for bomb-making. Fuel is a prime essential to power-makers; they do not see how they can take the many other risks without complete control of it.

Here, national defense and peacetime economics become badly confused. What price would the government guarantee for the fuel made by private plants? Would the demand be permanent? What about quality inspection? And in case of war could the government seize the plants altogether?

The breeder, it seems likely, will remain a government monopoly for a long time to come.

But it has become an important catalyst in speeding up

efforts in other directions, simply because it relieves the uncertainty of the long-range uranium supply. There will be atomic fuel enough for everything we need in the foreseeable future.

We have, then, a series of reactor designs beginning with the simple and bulky graphite-uranium pile and working down to the highly compact and specialized breeder. Dr. Lawrence Hafstad, who heads AEC's Reactor Development program, separates them into three classes, according to types of fuel— the reactor that uses straight uranium as nature makes it, the one that uses various degrees of 235-enriched material, and the breeder. He calls them the "burner-upper, the stretcher-outer and the breeder."

The burner-upper, explains Dr. Zinn, uses only a small fraction of the 235 in a charge of ordinary uranium—a fraction of the fractional 0.7 per cent of it originally present. Thus, practically 99.3 per cent of the fuel is thrown away. In the stretcher-outer, sometimes called the "converter," things are better. Here, as many as 80 per cent of the U-235 atoms can create plutonium, and they in turn 80 per cent *new* plutonium and so on in a diminishing series till all the fuel is used. The result is five times as much fission for a given original charge of 235, or a total of 3.5 per cent of the original supply. This is the stretching-out or regenerative process.

Now in the breeder, with its heart of pure U-235 and its surrounding blanket of U-238, and with its very high neutron economy, actually more fuel is created than is consumed. So, in theory, all the uranium of both isotopes can be used up—something better than 100 times as much heat from a given amount of fuel as in the earlier reactors.

Sensation-hunters looking for miracles won't find it in the breeder. But they will find it in the wonderful mental discipline which has made the breeder a fact.

II. Pilot Plant Stage

• • • • • • •

Now THAT we have some idea of how reactors work it may be interesting to glance at the ambitious plans of the commission for the next five years.

First, there is the large project to be carried out in Pennsylvania. The estimated cost of this is $85 million, with private capital taking on some $30 million of the obligation. If the 60,000-kilowatt output is realized the investment in the plant will be about $1350 per kilowatt. This is between four and five times the cost of conventional steam plants today, and at least three times the cost of hydroelectric installations. Therefore, it cannot possibly compete with them on an economic basis.

Congress originally hoped that private capital would do the whole job and put the American people into the experiment only when it was evident that industry did not dare risk so much while the law allowed them so little. But AEC felt much encouraged when the power interests suddenly offered to pay a third of the costs and take very large risks as well (they have donated the land, assumed much research expense and will buy the steam from the plant when it is running.

The great reactor will be of a compromise design, combining experiment with many well-tried features. Taking a calculated risk, the machine will use cooling water at the terrific pressure of 2000 pounds per square inch. Because of this extreme pressure the boiling point can be raised several hundred degrees above normal and the running temperature will be about 550 degrees. This means that the atomic reaction can proceed fairly rapidly in a small space without melting anything, and will give moderately good efficiency in the turbines. (A thousand degrees is becoming a common temperature in large electric plants nowadays—the atomic plant still has a long way to go.)

About 20 tons of slightly enriched uranium will be needed, and should last for several years. One interesting excursion into experiment will be the use of zirconium and hafnium alloys in the reactor structure and for control. Steel is practically useless at high atomic powers because its crystal structure is soon weakened by neutron bombardment so that it loses its strength. Also, steel is a savage neutron stealer. The only disadvantage of zirconium is that it is expensive and rare. An entire new industry must be built if it is to be supplied to very many reactors.

The Materials Testing Reactor in Idaho, which "discovered" zirconium, has also come up with a much-improved alloy of uranium that will not get mushy in a neutron atmosphere, at least not so soon. This is a second essential in the high-power machine, lengthening the time fuel metal can stay at work without having to go through the costly refining routine.

The primary purpose of this first full-sized power plant is to chase out "bugs." This is not only an engineering experiment; it is to show the entire industry how near we are to economic atom power. The question is, will such a machine work reliably enough to join the ultrareliable electric power network? If surprise problems turn up, now is the time to solve them.

The search for "bugs" suggests why this five-year exploration period will be of such intense interest to everyone connected with it. There will be a constant challenge in every phase of the work. Constant innovation is the price of prog ress.

Take the second AEC project, for instance. The plan is to build a 5000-kilowatt reactor of the boiling-water variety. This is the design that Dr. Zinn pointed out could not explode. The original experiments were made in 1953 with a very small machine. The principle called for surrounding the heat-producing core with water which would act both as neutron moderator and cooling medium. This water is pumped direct to a heat exchanger, where its heat turns a second supply of water into steam for the turbines. The neat trick is that if the reactor gets going too fast and produces too much heat, the cooling water boils and leaves the reactor. Lacking their moderator the neutrons immediately fly off and are lost; the chain reaction abruptly stops, the core cools down. This automatic control action takes place so fast that there is no possibility of a melt-down in the core.

In the large pilot model now to be built an even more ambitious innovation will be made. Why not do away with the heat exchanger altogether and allow the reactor to make steam directly for the turbines? There would be some gain in efficiency and a great deal of saving in pumps and other apparatus.

Thus, an important objective of this new boiling-water machine will be to find out what happens when radioactive steam is used in turbines and condensers in the main generating plant. Will the insides of the various devices be lined with lethal radioisotopes of oxygen? If they are, then a mere brokendown valve or a blown gasket might be as dangerous to repair as a live enemy bomb. So many of the early fears, however, are proving groundless as experience increases, that this one, too, may be eliminated. This new plant, to go into service in 1956, will give us many of the answers.

Third of the group of projects is a big-scale experiment with liquid-metal cooling, combined with a first try at using thorium and uranium as a composite fuel. It will also be tried on enriched uranium, running as a converter to generate some plutonium. Although not a real breeder, it will automatically pass over from uranium to plutonium somewhere along the way, and test out the expectations of greatly increased "burnup period"—or life.

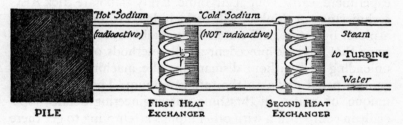

The problem of burnup in an atomic reactor is a very serious one on the economic side—as serious as how often you must fill the tank of your car. In the reactor's case it is not an empty tank but a tank choked with ashes that is bad. In the converter the ashes can be tolerated for a much longer time.

When thorium is used this third pilot plant is expected to become a breeder in a small way, thus extending the life cycle still more. North American Aviation, Inc., in California, are taking over this particular job. They have already built two small research reactors for neutron production. Neither produces appreciable power but they have the distinction of being the first in the world built by private interests. The complete reactor fits into a space no bigger than a two-car garage, and will operate day-in-day-out for ten years without refueling. In that time only five per cent of the fuel will have been consumed.

In the big North American reactor, to be finished in 1956, temperatures are to be investigated. Designers are intending to push the liquid metal to 1250 degrees, instead of the 1000 degrees so far considered the limit. This will mean a great improvement in the cost of power. And costs are among the main issues to be settled in this drive to make the atom compete with present-day fuels.

Most promising of the series, it is hoped, will be the first full-sized breeder, a machine expected to turn out 15,000 kilowatts of electric energy. This will be a strictly all-government experiment, carried out at Argonne. Every elaborate trick AEC technicians can think of will be included. Dr. Zinn, who is an explorer by nature, will watch innumerable cut-and-try innovations that have no precedent at all: methods of loading and unloading fuel without dismantling the machine, systems of control pared down to the safe minimum. There is nothing unique, of course, in thrashing out engineering details, especially in competition with other groups attempting to get there first. But this time AEC has a special motive. It would like to get the drop on Russia in this most promising field.

12. Jules Verne—1955

· · · · · · · ·

WE COME now to the already famous submarine projects, the *Nautilus* and the *Sea Wolf*. Strange as a Jules Verne fiction, it is in the depths of the sea that atomic power is to have its first real use. AEC hopes it will be a prime warning to any enemy that a new day has begun in naval warfare. We are none too far ahead, for it is reported that Russia is racing us in this field as well.

The *Nautilus* was launched at Groton, Conn., on January 21, 1954, and by now is making her trial runs. The *Sea Wolf* is about two years behind. Still other atomic subs are planned.

With all the notoriety and evil reputation the submarine has gathered in some 40 years of operations, there has never been a "real" one. All subs so far have been primarily surface vessels that were tight and strong enough to travel briefly under water. Their below-surface existence has been temporary and difficult; because of their prime requirement of oxygen for their diesel engines they have been limited to brief runs on storage batteries when submerged. Their speed below has been very poor—10 to 12 knots. At best they have had an underwater cruising range of less than 100 miles.

The *Nautilus*, however, will be a *true* submarine vessel, as her creator, Rear Admiral Hyman G. Rickover, has dubbed her. Her atomic engines require no oxygen, and so can turn out full power beneath the sea for as long as the fuel lasts. The uranium charge is said to be sufficient for 30,000 miles, and the *Nautilus* can use it all up without surfacing at all. The ship's hull is deliberately shaped for underwater travel, streamlined like a fish. Actually, it is considerably more efficient than any surface vessel below the surface. Standard subs are of a compromise design, to cut down surface wave-making as much as possible. The atomic sub's place is *in* the sea, not *on* it.

This fishlike efficiency shows up in extraordinary speed. The *Nautilus* is designed to cruise down under at 20 knots and can do 25 with the control rods full out. This is close to 30 miles an hour—faster than most fish.

Simple as it may sound to design and build, the *Nautilus* was not an easy achievement.

Seagoing experts like to boast that the atomic submarine is the greatest single advance in naval vessels in perhaps 100 years. In the light of this it is amazing to find that the project required a major struggle against every kind of human as well as physical odds. The brass were at first utterly indifferent to the proposal. Then they said it couldn't be done and finally some of them made extraordinary efforts to prevent its being done.

The *Nautilus* was Rickover's idea and he drove her through in the course of five years, bucking the Navy, the AEC and industry until, one by one they capitulated. Rickover's story is dramatically told in a recent book by Clay Blair of TIME magazine. It is a book everyone should read.

Atomic propulsion for the Navy was discussed far back in the war. The Tolman Committee, a group of advisory scientists, urged it in 1944. The scheme was properly turned down then; there was neither time nor talent to spare from the bomb.

After the war atomic energy fell into a vacuum between military and civilian control. When the civilians finally won, under the Atomic Energy Act, they were so overwhelmed with the job that they spent several years getting organized. Many of the brilliant scientists of war days had left. It was all the commission could do to maintain bomb construction.

Gradually, AEC scientists got restive at the preoccupation with bombs. Such men as Edward Teller at Los Alamos and Lawrence Hafstad in Washington and Enrico Fermi, now at the University of Chicago, wanted atomic power investigated. All three felt that naval applications would be a good place to start. Then Captain Rickover, an engineering officer in the Navy's Bureau of Ships, injected himself into the scene.

Rickover's contention was that atomic drive was ideal for submarines. From a propulsion point of view they were the weakest link in naval defense. He insisted that a reactor would fit into a sub's hull and make her the most deadly of all fighting vessels. The job, he maintained, could be done and done fast; it was 95 per cent engineering and only five per cent science.

Rickover did not originate the idea of an atomic submarine. It had started in the fertile brain of Charles A. Thomas, president of the Monsanto Chemical Company. Monsanto had operated a large section of Oak Ridge during the war; now in peacetime Thomas urged that a group of men be gathered from the services and trained at Oak Ridge to tackle the problems of atomic power. No one was much interested, but finally the Navy did send eight men to a kind of atom school there. The leader of this little "task force" had been chosen because he was a restless man in search of new achievement, and a nuisance to the Navy. It was Rickover.

A year's technical study at an intense pace served to weld the little group together, convincing Rick that the submarine was the place to start. It did little else. The Washington brass had lost interest. Various industrial concerns, notably General Electric, had other fish to fry. Even Monsanto no longer seemed to care. But Rickover, once started, would not let go. This was in 1947. Returning to Washington he began to pull wires to get his ambitious submarine program started, stoutly contending it was purely an engineering job.

The Navy answered by removing Rick from atomic matters, putting another officer in charge of a vague thing called the "Nuclear Project." Rickover countered by concocting a letter for Chief of Naval Operations Nimitz to send to the Secretary of the Navy. With great persistence he finally got it cleared. Nimitz was delighted and signed it at once.

Nothing happened. Rick wrote another letter, to the AEC. It was ignored. He wrote again and was again pigeonholed. Finally he got a break through his friend Admiral Mills, who was induced to make a speech (which Rickover wrote), criticizing AEC for stalling on atomic power. The result was that the commission was forced to organize a Department of Reactor Development. Rick's good friend Hafstad was put in charge. He himself became the Navy's liaison to it.

Captain Rickover immediately put pressure on General Electric to begin work on naval atomic designs. G.E. was reluctant, being more interested in the breeder reactor. Rick quickly switched to Westinghouse and after months of talk got them started on a study of submarine-type power plants.

People admired Rickover but were uneasy with him. He was dynamic, ruthless, demanding. And he knew as much about atomic engineering as any man alive. No problem was too large or too tricky for his little group at the Bureau of Ships, self-trained, every one. Breathlessly and often appalled, the cautious industrial engineers were forced to undertake "the impossible." Couldn't this four-striper realize that the war was over?

But they usually found that Rick was right. An example was zirconium. When he learned that it was an ideal metal for reactor construction he demanded it for his submarine. The engineers objected that it cost $450,000 a pound and that there weren't 20 pounds of it in the U.S. He forced them to organize large-scale production, bring down the cost and produce it by the ton. The same thing happened with hafnium, then a laboratory curiosity.

Slowly the Westinghouse people picked up enthusiasm and finally became as eager for the submarine as Rickover himself. High executives were enrolled in a "nuclear school" which he organized. The submarine project was all at once first priority business at Westinghouse.

The Argonne Laboratory now came into the picture. Dr. Zinn had also taken fire from Rickover. One of his most valuable contributions was the insistence that a land-based submarine power plant be built first, in the desert at Arco, Idaho, and run at full throttle for exhaustive tests. As a result, two nearly identical machines were laid down, the Mark I prototype at Arco, the Mark II seagoing reactor in Pittsburgh.

Rick was a glutton for testing. He was determined that the *Nautilus* should be the world's best and safest undersea vessel. When the Navy depth-charged the old submarine Ulua in Chesapeake Bay to test a host of new ideas, Rick had a large compartment of the boat filled with components of the new atomic engine. Particularly, he wanted to redesign the shock resistance of delicate apparatus such as meters, controls and electric equipment. He was able to make many important improvements in landlubber-designed gadgets under these simulated battle conditions.

By 1950 the project was taking shape in earnest. In a large, windowless concrete building at Arco, Westinghouse was installing an actual duplicate of the atomic end of the *Nautilus*. It was a steel shell of full ship's diameter, containing the reactor, shielding, piping, heat exchangers, pumps, and at the after end, the steam turbines that would drive one of the boat's two propellers. The whole assembly was contained in a large tank that could be filled with 50 feet of sea water, to simulate the exact shielding conditions to be met in service. The building of this "mock-up" was a long, painful job—a "learner," actually—in which every part was studied and fitted and tested before going in.

Some of the work involved radioactive materials and had to be done behind seven feet of concrete by remote control. In other cases the subassembly work was carried on 25 feet down in a tank of water. A typical fussy job was the welding of the zirconium parts, which had to be done in a large vacuum cylinder resembling an iron lung. Welded in air zirconium would pick up oxygen and make poor joints.

A prime difficulty in this first seagoing power reactor has been the purity of materials. Every element has its own special behavior with neutrons. Unfortunately, metallic impurities are legion and always present; they have the bad habit of picking up radioactivity. Especially bad actors are cadmium and boron, common contaminants of steel. In this exceedingly compact reactor even minute traces could not be tolerated. Such purity of materials was a must. It had to be attained by refinement more exacting than that in a medical laboratory.

In the cooling water there was another danger of radioactivity. Circulating in so confined a space as a sub's engine room, it must be wholly free of impurities that would store up radiation. Thus, the engineers had to learn how to provide hundreds of gallons of water even purer than the finest distilled drinking water.

In May, 1953, the landlocked engine was finally completed and full-power tests were begun there in the desert. With something like 25,000 horsepower to deal with, the power was absorbed by a giant friction brake, cooled by water which in turn was pumped outdoors to a large spray pond. Here, 22,000 gallons a minute were forced through an acre of nozzles, losing their heat to the desert air.

While every conceivable thing was being done at Arco to iron out the bugs, Mark II moved along in the Westinghouse plant in the east. Rickover likes to call it "a very fine Swiss watch built to large size"—almost literally true. Never before had a machine as big as a house had to be built to the exacting tolerances of a precision instrument. This was partly at the insistence of Rickover himself, with his passion for making things work *right*. And it was partly the able hand of Zinn and his Argonne associates, and of Charlie Weaver, the Westinghouse nuclear engineering chief. But mainly it was the new standard which craftsmen will have to meet as common practice in the atomic age.

The largest and most concentrated force known to man is created by one of the smallest known subdivisions of matter. Successful behavior of the machines depends on incredible purity of materials, absolute dimensional accuracy, infallible control, the exact teaming up of each part with every other. It is a new order of engineering, and it is the Navy's pride that a seagoing engineer should be the first to accomplish it.

13. "Hell or High Water"
• • • • • • • • • • •

THE NATION will never know how much it owes to a little group of men who worked literally day and night for five years to put atomic power under the sea. Certainly the Navy did not appreciate them. For Rickover, in the midst of his great project, was snubbed by the brass. The ponderous Selection Board, choosing its annual list of captains to be promoted to rear admiral, "passed him over."

Rickover ignored the slight. Many of his friends guessed that it was no oversight, but an intentional affront. Rick had never kowtowed to his superiors nor indulged in bootlicking. He had never gone by the book. When he wanted something done fast he could be very embarrassing indeed.

This was in 1951. A year later, with the keel of the *Nautilus* on the ways, he was passed over again. A peculiar wrinkle in Navy protocol says that a captain twice rejected for promotion must resign within a year. Suddenly it was no longer a question of personal spite. In effect, the fusty admirals of the Board had given notice that engineering brilliance in this age of science is less important to our armed forces than correct military behavior. Their brother officers in the Air Force had done the same thing to Billy Mitchell and had made it stick—temporarily. This new stiff-backed lot planned to do the same.

But they had misjudged the American people for whom they worked. A tremendous storm of protest arose. Hundreds of articles and editorials blossomed in the nation's press; industrialists who had been badgered and harassed by Rickover for years wrote to Congress in his defense. Pressure was put on the Secretary of the Navy, on the AEC, on the President. It was all ignored—apparently. Then a single small voice was heard in the House of Representatives. Yates of Illinois courageously took the Navy to task.

Late in 1952, as the administration was about to change, Yates launched his charges on the House floor. Eisenhower, coming to Washington, found he had inherited a *cause célèbre.* Congress let his advisers know that unless the Navy rectified its mistake a full-fledged investigation would ensue. Quietly, the new President pulled the strings. In the summer of '53 Rickover became an admiral.

His friends had won and the victory over Navy protocol probably saved the atomic submarine from a delay of many years. This was not merely important to one man. It was known by then that Russia was straining every sinew to get an atomic sub into the water before we did. Stupidity had been prevented from operating against the public interest.

What exactly is the *Nautilus?* She is a 300-foot steel fish with a skin so thick and a structure so strong that she can dive to unheard-of depths, into dim regions where few enemy depth charges can find her. More than 1000 feet down she can maneuver swiftly and silently, seeking out her victims with a special sonar which will permit her captain to "see" them on a screen, then doing them in with the latest electronic torpedoes that find their own targets. Having released them she can be miles away before the surface pack even begin looking for her. The only craft she really has to fear is another atomic sub like herself.

Rickover already knew submarines intimately when he designed her: he understood the torture of long confinement in cramped quarters and steadily worsening air. It was his idea to design the *Nautilus'* interior in comparative luxury. Although the reactor and driving machinery take up half the hull space, there is room for special quarters for chief petty officers (as well as officers) and game rooms for the crew. The matter of good air has received special attention too. The most advanced air-conditioning equipment will keep temperatures moderate and air dry, while newly invented "scrubbers" will hold the carbon dioxide content far below the lethal three per cent. Fresh oxygen will be made directly from sea water—something no other submarine can do. Air as fine in quality as that on the surface is expected to take the last serious handicap from the submarine service.

Then there will be deep-freeze lockers and other equipment for serving the best possible meals. The interior will even be painted in soft, pleasant colors. With such attention to comfort as this, the boat can cruise for months, if necessary, without once coming up.

To make sure that his plans for crew comfort were sound, Rickover had a special group of 22 men and officers spend six weeks submerged at a New London dock in a sub fitted with the new devices. They came out as fresh and in as good psychological condition as they went in. The "trip" was even joked about in the press. A cartoonist showed the *Nautilus* surfacing at a dock. An annoyed admiral is standing there. "Why are they coming up?" he demands. "They have to come up every three months to re-enlist," replies an aide.

The atomic machinery of the *Nautilus* is a marvel of compactness that should have a profound influence on the effective design of all future reactors. The heart of the atomic pile, with its charge of enriched uranium, is contained in a massive high-pressure drum, built to withstand 2000 pounds per square inch. Highly purified cooling water, pumped through it at this pressure, carries the intense heat of fission out to the heat exchanger, where it makes steam for the turbines, at 600 degrees.

A heat exchanger, it might be noted, is merely a special boiler—a tight container filled with metal tubes. Hot water from the pile circulates through these tubes, which are surrounded by the steaming water. Thus the upper part of the container is charged with high-pressure steam. According to Admiral Rickover, these heat exchangers are nearly 100 per cent efficient in transferring heat. The only loss of consequence is in the pumps needed to force water in and out of the reactor at the great pressure required.

The *Nautilus* will carry enough fuel to send her around the globe without a stop (the Mark I prototype has just finished such a "cruise" in Idaho, 500 miles from the sea). When she has finally exhausted her fuel supply, a short lay-over in a special dock will suffice to renew it. Naturally, all details of this process are confidential.

When the sub is under way, every sort of safety device will protect her crew, including a "scram light." If this flashes on the men will leave the vicinity of the reactor and the boat will surface in a hurry. It will mean that something has gone wrong inside the shielding. It may never be lighted.

The designers of the *Nautilus* believed that the best protection would be that which was simplest. Thus, a handful of men can operate the atomic plant. In a serious emergency a single pair of hands can work all essential controls.

Lead is the principal shielding material because it is the most economical of space for its weight. When Rick was toiling in the midst of his worst design problems he was besieged with helpful suggestions, many of them from people outside the Navy. One persistent man kept urging him to shield the sub's reactor with gold from Fort Knox. It might as well be doing something useful, he said. After arguing a long time, Rick declined wearily. Gold would be fine, he admitted, as it is denser than lead. But it would take all the treasure in our vaults to supply this one sub. And suppose the vessel sank?

Shielding is no simple problem in so confined a space. Not only must the crew be protected from the radioactive heart of the pile itself, but from all high-pressure piping, heat exchangers and pumps. All of these vital components must be sealed tightly within the lead shield, *and cannot be serviced if anything goes wrong.* One of the hardest problems to solve in all atomic engines is to design quite ordinary parts such as pumps and valves so that they will never need repair. Evidently it has been solved on the *Nautilus,* no doubt by a combination of remarkable design and the provision of duplicate or even triplicate parts so that a standby can take over automatically when an operating part fails.

The achievement of an atomic submarine means much more than a new chapter in naval armaments. The *Nautilus'* engines are not so special that they cannot be copied in many respects for civilian use. In fact, Rickover and Westinghouse both have gone on into the next logical step: applying what they have learned to the problems of the big Duquesne power plant. For Rickover is in charge of the project for AEC, and Westinghouse has built an entire new plant to produce it and other atomic equipment.

One thing should be noted clearly: an atomic submarine

is a military job. There has been no attempt to bring its power plant down to cost levels competitive with ordinary seagoing engines. No ship owner could afford to install $15 million boilers in his vessels, even in ocean liners, let alone doing so in a ship only 300 feet long. Such an outlay is justified for the Navy because the huge costs will buy us a new degree of national security, just as the astronomical outlays in atomic bombs have done. But the *Nautilus* does not mean that an atomic merchant marine is the next logical step. The economics of it have got to be ironed out first. We shall see how well this can be done in a later section.

Free of economic limitations, atomic power is already very attractive. In fact, in 1950, it was promising enough so that the Navy's CNO asked Rickover's group to design the power plant for a supercarrier. A good start was made; Westinghouse received a contract to start work on the engines; a shipbuilder was designated. Then the project was canceled. Even for the Navy an atomic carrier was too costly.

The work on this "CVR" reactor wasn't scrapped, however. Rick was smart enough to use it in the Duquesne plant designs.

A word about the *Sea Wolf*, now pretty well along. In basic concept she is said to be not very different from the *Nautilus*. The main departure is a technical one in the new reactor. *Sea Wolf's* engines are designated as the "SIR," while her earlier sister's are called the "STR." The "I" and the "T" refer to the condition of the neutrons within the reactors. T is for "thermal" and I for "intermediate." Thermal neutrons have been completely slowed down by a moderator to speeds comparable to the slow thermal motions of molecules at room temperature—a few miles per second. Intermediate velocity particles travel at some thousands of miles per second.

At the very high velocities at which neutrons are born in

fission, uranium-238 has what is called a resonance for them: it captures them avidly. To avoid this when much 238 is present, bulky moderators must be used to cut down neutron speed as quickly as possible. If the fuel is greatly enriched to eliminate most of the U-238, the neutrons will remain uncaptured even at intermediate speeds quite close to resonance. Thus, moderator bulk can be much smaller. In the bomb there is no moderator, for there is no 238 at all.

In the *Sea Wolf*'s SIR reactor the compromise requires more costly fuel but less space. Further to "soup up" the engine, liquid-metal cooling is used and much higher operating temperatures are available. Hence better efficiency and perhaps more power.

It was not deemed wise to make this long step in the first sub, which was fitted with more "conventional" reactor and equipment. Navy and AEC hope that by the time the *Sea Wolf* is ready for trial the *Nautilus* will have furnished enough basic experience to make the longer gamble pay off.

Almost the only publicized feature of the SIR project so far is the gigantic steel sphere in which the testing of the prototype, Mark A, is being done. The purpose of this is to protect the countryside in case a sodium blowup occurs. Testing of the Mark I in Idaho proved to be a severe inconvenience; it was an example of leaning over backward to insure safety. General Electric convinced the AEC that it would cost less and save time to build this spherical testing laboratory within a few miles of Schenectady, N.Y.

The ball, made of welded steel plates an inch and a half thick, stands in a 40,000-acre plot cleared of all inhabitants. It is 225 feet in diameter. Inside there will be a great tank of sea water, as there was in Idaho. Much the same test schedule will be followed as with Mark I, including long "cruises" deeply submerged.

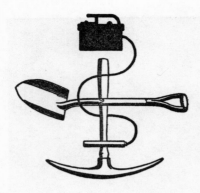

14. Forty-Niners of the 20th Century

• • • • • •

REACTORS LIE cold and helpless without their charges of uranium. We will stop for a moment to see how the fuel is mined and prepared. The story, so far released, deals only with uranium. Thorium, soon to be important, is still under wraps.

Almost everyone has heard of the Geiger counter and knows that it is an instrument for detecting the radioactivity of hidden uranium. In the past ten years literally thousands of miners, and a great many amateurs too, have fitted themselves with these and more delicate instruments and have gone prospecting for the new metal which is so much more valuable than gold.

So anxious is the AEC to discover new domestic sources of uranium that it has a standing offer of $10,000 to anyone—individual or company—who produces from a new deposit at least 20 tons of ore bearing at least 20 per cent uranium oxide. The bonus is *in addition* to the guaranteed price paid for the ore itself. At the present average figure of $3.50 per pound of oxide content, one could make a small fortune—well over $40,000— in a short time, if one included AEC's haulage allowance and the value of the vanadium and other metals likely to be in the ore.

The bonus has some strings, of course. It does not apply to the carnotite and roscoelite minerals common to the famous Colorado Plateau, where most uranium is found in the United States. But there are other bonuses designed to keep the lucky prospector working at top speed once he has made a strike.

In ten years nobody has captured the big prize; there is evidently little top-grade ore in the country. Most of the mineral being mined today assays at about $\frac{2}{10}$ of 1 per cent uranium oxide and brings the miner from $10 to $60 a ton.

Nor is the search at all easy. The Colorado Plateau, scene of this 20th-century bonanza, is an area of 130,000 square miles, lying about equally in the states of Colorado, Utah, New Mexico and Arizona. It is mostly arid desert, cut by deep canyons and mesas many thousands of feet high that are virtually inaccessible. There are few roads; the area is 7000 feet above sea level and subject to prolonged winter blizzards and violent summer cloudbursts. It is no place for a week-ender in the family car.

Nevertheless, this new kind of treasure hunting should interest every lover of the outdoors, for uranium can appear anywhere and can be found with a counter costing no more than $100. The telltale little blinks of the neon lamp on the instrument have already led to valuable deposits in other Rocky Mountain states, in California, Michigan and Pennsylvania. Uranium claims have even been filed at Camp Smith, N.Y. Fabulously rich deposits lie to the north of us in Canada. The AEC gets out a little book for 30¢—*Prospecting For Uranium* —which tells anyone how to go about using a Geiger counter, where to look for uranium and what to do when you think you've found it.

American ores are mostly the powdery yellow carnotite, which occurs in the sedimentary deposits of the great plateau country. This is known as a "secondary" ore, having been leached away by water from primary deposits in igneous rock. The canary yellow or brown "gold" is found mostly in elusive horizontal strata sandwiched between sedimentary layers, often high on the mesa cliffs and well out of reach. But sometimes it appears in the middle of a field or on an easy hillside.

Carnotite was first discovered at Naturita, Colorado, in 1899, and quickly became famous when the Curies exported it to Paris for their radium separation work. The ore got its name from M. Carnot, then president of France.

More than 500 mines are producing on the Plateau today, and the area is jammed with thousands of people. All the lurid history of the fabulous overnight wealth, claim-jumping, legal battles and vigilantes of 1849, is being repeated with counting instruments instead of gold pans. Only very expensive "scintillation counters" will find ore that is deeply hidden, so the little man is confined to surface prospecting unless he is willing to sink tunnels on a pure gamble.

For preliminary exploration, AEC and its private contractors drill hundreds of thousands of feet of core holes every year, boring deep to see what may lie out of reach of any counter. Survey work is also done with delicate instruments flown over the area at 50 feet or so—a dangerous business but one that has yielded enormous returns. AEC is rapidly building surfaced roads to open up the area.

Notwithstanding all the hardships and the technical advantages enjoyed by the large operators there have been fantastic strikes by completely penniless people. The case of Paddy Martinez, a New Mexican Indian, is typical. Paddy carried a piece of carnotite around for months, not knowing what it was. When a mining expert finally followed it up, Paddy found himself the discoverer of one of the richest carnotite deposits in America—on the right of way of the Santa Fe Railroad. The now-celebrated Haystack Mine, near Grants, N.M., has already turned out more than $2 million in good ore. The railroad settled a lifetime annuity on Paddy and built him his first house, which the Martinez family find a constant embarrassment.

Most celebrated of all, probably, are Charlie Steen, now said to be worth millions, and Vernon Pick. Pick was marooned on an island in a flooded river with a broken ankle when he realized that rock he had found was probably carnotite. After two days of terror and fighting with rattlesnakes, he escaped, scaled a cliff and let down his scintillometer by a rope tied to his foot. The ore was there, as he proved by reading the instrument through field glasses.

The story goes that Vernon had borrowed $400 from each of two friends to grubstake himself. He finally paid up the loans with two checks for a million dollars each. Pick modestly admitted to me that he has a bank account in seven figures after a couple of years' work, but he thinks of nothing but to keep on working till he "really strikes it rich."

Uranium, like gold, is where you find it. Most people don't. A few get rich; everybody, apparently, keeps happy.

There are quacks in the uranium racket, too. The mails are flooded with come-ons for get-rich-quick mining stocks, mostly from Canada. And one or two shysters have lured thousands to abandoned workings where they claim slight radioactivity will benefit the sick. The law has caught up with some but there will be others as long as there are suckers.

The sudden demand for uranium in 1940 found this country with almost none. It was even being thrown away in the refining of vanadium and radium on the Plateau. Unable to wait for domestic production the government imported great quantities of much richer ores from Belgium and Canada. Belgium owns by far the richest known uranium deposits, in the remote Shinkelobwe mines of the Congo. Shinkelobwe is 800 miles deep in equatorial Africa, in a wild jungle region. But the Belgians, always friendly to us, gladly developed the mines. Without their co-operation we probably would not have had a bomb in 1945.

High-grade uranium ore seems always inaccessible. Canada's Eldorado mine on Great Bear Lake in Northwest Territory lies athwart the Arctic Circle, reachable only by air most of the year. Nevertheless, Canada's own atomic project depends on it, and the mine gave us important support during the war. Lately a great new uranium boom has started at Lake Athabaska, 500 miles nearer civilization but still virtually inaccessible.

The great importance of the Canadian and African deposits is that they produce pitchblende, a gray-black igneous rock which is almost all uranium oxide. This is a "primary" mineral, laid down when the earth was formed. Pitchblende is what AEC hopes to find here at home.

The only other known source of pitchblende—unless Russia has found one and kept it secret—is the ancient workings at Joachimsthal in Czechoslovakia. During the war the Germans seized it and worked it desperately until their bomb project collapsed. At war's end, unfortunately, Russia inherited it and has exploited it mercilessly with slave labor.

AEC runs a highly organized uranium procurement business based on Grand Junction, Colorado. This includes careful mapping and exploring of the whole plateau area, the maintaining of assay and purchasing stations, the promotion of research in ore processing, the improvement of access roads. Anyone who wants to gamble on this modern gold rush will find the government most willing to help him.

The government is even beginning to exploit very poor ores as a by-product of other mining work. Soon after the war it entered into an agreement with the British to purchase recovered uranium from the vast gold mine dumps in South Africa. We are getting important quantities there now. Recently, Australian sources have been developed in which we are also interested. At home, we are doing the same thing with phosphate deposits in Texas and Florida. Recoverable amounts of uranium oxide can thus be obtained from the fertilizer industry at costs far less than if the ore were worked for uranium alone.

In the long run what AEC hopes to do is to create a fuel supply that will be independent of all foreign help and still cheap enough to be feasible if a war should cut us off completely.

Once domestic uranium sources have been discovered the

ore is mined by individuals and by private companies on a profit basis. AEC buys all uranium oxide ore at a guaranteed price but permits it to remain in private hands while it is refined. The end product is U_3O_8—the common oxide. The miners and smelters may keep for themselves any by-products such as vanadium oxide, silver, copper and lead.

Now the government takes over in the preparation of basic "feed material." This is a carefully controlled chemical operation that removes all impurities. The next step leads to uranium fluoride (UF_4), known as "green salt." The route now divides. Part of the salt disappears into the giant diffusion plants where the two isotopes of the metal are pried apart; the remainder is turned into slugs of metal of top purity for use in the plutonium piles. By this time secrecy has descended. AEC builds its own plants and contracts for their operation under rigid supervision.

15. Battle of the Isotopes

• • • • • • • • • •

THERE HAS never been a more remarkable achievement in technology than the separation of two kinds of uranium whose only difference is a one per cent variation in weight. Chemically they are identical, so that the only hope of separating them lies in exploiting the property known as mass.

In the early 40's four possible methods were tried: separation by mass spectrograph, by centrifugal action, by diffusion in hot solution, and by diffusion as a gas through porous barriers. The first and last proved equally feasible, the other two were dropped after exhaustive research. Today, gaseous diffusion is the standard method.

Under the direction of Dr. E. O. Lawrence, inventor of the cyclotron, magnetic separation was undertaken at full scale at Oak Ridge. Giant magnets were constructed and energized with hundreds of thousands of kilowatts of electricity. Natural uranium was fed through an electron gun into the magnetic field at enormous speed. Atoms of the two isotopes, being minutely different in weight, followed slightly different paths and were collected in separate "bins." The thin stream, a few million atoms thick, had to flow for months before visible amounts of the isotopes accrued. Nevertheless, the giant fac-

93

tories of "Y-12" at Oak Ridge collected enough pure U-235 to fill the first bombs.

After the war the magnetic separation plant was demobilized in favor of diffusion, which had also been at work in "K-25" at Oak Ridge. Today, K-25 has been greatly enlarged and two new plants, at Paducah, Ky., and Portsmouth, O., have been added. It takes many square miles of factory to produce grams of the precious U-235.

The principle of gaseous diffusion is that if two gases of slightly different atomic weight are driven through barriers with very small holes, the lighter atoms get through a little more readily than the heavier. By repeating the process over and over the lighter gas gradually enriches, while the heavier stays behind.

With incredible courage the top men of the bomb project authorized this complicated method of outwitting nature. Only one element combines with uranium to form a gas—fluorine—one of the worst actors in all chemistry. Fluorine will form compounds with almost any element but will leave it instantly if something more attractive turns up. A famous scientist likens fluorine to a predatory young man walking down the street with a pretty girl, eying all the other girls the while. If a prettier one comes along, off he goes to her.

Unfortunately, uranium, in the eyes of fluorine, is not too attractive a companion and is in critical danger of abandonment at any moment. Chemically speaking, UF_6 is a highly active gas and will attack almost anything. Called "hex," it is viciously corrosive of all metals. Worse, the gas won't diffuse at all unless it is very hot, which makes it more active than ever.

Because of the very slight separation through any one barrier, there must be thousands in series—many acres of them—and these present such a resistance that the hex has to be driven through them by thousands of pumps of a kind that won't leak or corrode. A leak anywhere would be suicidal to the project and deadly to humans. Superelaborate systems of leak detection were invented for the diffusion plant, working automatically and able to pinpoint trouble on the instant and raise the alarm.

At first corrosion difficulties seemed insuperable. Two inventions saved the day. The first was a new type of gas pump operated by magnetism. The second was a major advance in chemistry: a whole family of new compounds known as fluorocarbons, that were entirely indifferent to fluorine itself. Chemists found that once fluorine is tightly bound to another element it can become completely inert, so tightly locked in that practically nothing will disturb it. In many secret uses of these compounds of fluorine and carbon at Oak Ridge, piping, gaskets and valves were made impervious to the corrosive gas.

As a by-product, a whole new field in organic chemistry has been opened up. Starting with the familiar Freon, the original fluorocarbon developed by Du Pont, the family promises to produce a host of materials indifferent to corrosion, rust, heat, light and many other diseases of modern use.

The barriers in the diffusion plant were an amazing achievement. There must be billions of holes not much big-

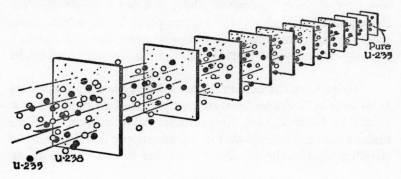

ger than the molecules themselves. They must be uniform and easily replaced when they plug up. Here was one of the top secrets of the process. Several years were spent finding a suitable material and learning to make it just porous enough to work. Nothing has been said about the final product except that its holes are less than four ten-millionths of an inch in diameter. Like the fluorocarbons it will probably find use as superfilter material in many industries.

At Oak Ridge the barriers were arranged in series, installed in buildings that have been called the largest industrial structures in the world. The uranium gas, however, did not travel from one end to the other but was constantly "recycled" to hasten the process of enrichment. That is, some of it was withdrawn partway through and bled back into earlier stages, thus improving the U-235 content. This was still not very fast. It took a U-235 atom several months to make the journey and emerge in the exclusive company of its purified companions. And of course after the trip was done the fluorine that had "gone along for the ride" had to be pried loose, so that actual uranium metal could be made.

Breakdown in any part of the system could not be tolerated, for if anything failed the entire line would stall and it might take months to get it into action again. In a unique triumph of engineering control, there was not a single stop for three years. Yet here was the biggest plant in the world, using more current than New York and more water than the nation's capital—a plant whose active interior no human hand could touch.

These fantastic demands drained every available kilowatt from near-by TVA and private companies, then required new plants be built at Oak Ridge itself. All were tied together under such rigid control that if any one supply failed automatic switches shifted the burden to another in less than a thousandth of a second. No such requirement had ever been put upon electrical engineers before. The necessity for meeting it has put some parts of the industry years ahead.

AEC's two new diffusion plants in Kentucky and Ohio are so large that an entirely new electric system has been built to supply them alone. The commission's uranium operations today use four times the electricity supplied to New York City; the bomb program is now the largest single user of electricity in the world.

Inside the diffusion plants are many hundreds of manual controls, operated by a small army of people, many of whom tend one indicator and nothing else. In wartime only a handful of top men knew what was going on; the rest had learned not to be curious. They knew that the Army was "making something," and let it go at that.

There is a story of a harassed department head who one day found a young girl knob-turner asleep on her job. He woke her up summarily and gave her a good bawling out. Didn't she know that she held a vital place in the scheme? "When I want six," he growled, "you set your dial on six and do it fast. If I want ten, get on the ball and give me ten. The same with nine or five or—"

The girl yawned. "Look, mister," she drawled in a golden southern voice, "when you make up your mind what setting you want I'll give it to you. Not until!"

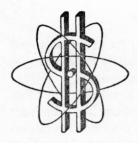

16. A Touch of Economics
• • • • • • • • • •

THE ECONOMICS of atomic fuels are quite as interesting as their technology, and not nearly so secret. The minute the first bomb was dropped President Truman announced that it had the force of 20,000 tons of TNT. He had been told to say it, of course. What was meant was that the bomb released as much heat as that quantity of old-style explosive. Engineers could have told you that this was also equivalent to 24,000,000 kilowatt-hours of energy, or 82 thousand million British thermal units (B.t.u.'s).

The bomb created a new energy unit, the *kiloton equivalent*, the original explosion being rated at 20. The hydrogen bomb has brought still another, the *megaton equivalent*, meaning *millions* of tons of TNT. Peacetime atomic power has little use for these fantastic figures. So we go back to the kilowatt and B.t.u. One B.t.u. will heat a pint of water one degree in one minute. A kilowatt-minute (of heat) will do 57 times as much; a kilowatt-hour, 3415 times as much. Remembering that kilowatt-hours and B.t.u.'s are units of quantity (or work), we are ready for the following staggering figures:

The burning of a pound of good coal produces about 14,000 B.t.u.; a pound of 100-octane gasoline about 22,000. This means that a pound of uranium fuel is roughly equal to 1300 *tons* of coal or about 300,000 gallons of gasoline. It is this vast advantage in weight that makes atomic power so attractive. One little cube of U-235, an inch on a side, weighs a pound. It would outlast a coal pile that would fill your whole back yard; it would (if it could be used) power twenty automobiles for their natural lives.

Admiral Rickover once explained that if any reactor "burns" one gram of U-235 it produces 24,000 kilowatt-hours of heat. A pound of the stuff would turn out 10,896,000 of them. He cautioned, however, that no power plant will recover much more than ¼ of the heat as electric current, so your pound of fuel would deliver some 2,724,000 kilowatt-hours to a propeller or power line.

Playing with the figures a little further it appears that if your reactor used up a pound of fuel a day, as in a vessel, you would get a power *rate* of about 113,500 kilowatts, or better than 150,000 horsepower. Such a vessel would be a blue-ribbon ocean liner or a supercarrier—on a cube of uranium the size of a child's building block! Burned in a central electric plant that cube would run a major city for 24 hours.

The picture is not quite so rosy when we look at price. Coal now ranges around $10 a ton in bulk. A good half of that is transportation cost, and in coal-hungry areas it can be $15 a ton or more. Some years ago Dr. Hafstad guessed that $20 a gram was a modest price for U-235. If we take $30 to be conservative now, a pound of atomic fuel would come to $13,620 (there are 454 grams in a pound). Reckoning 1300 tons of coal to be equivalent to this pound of U-235, in power-producing ability, $10-a-ton coal would cost about the same. However, all the uranium cannot be used up; when a small percentage has gone the whole charge must be removed and cleansed of fission products. This expensive process adds about 100 per cent to the actual price of the fuel. Thus, while a modern coal-burning station reckons its fuel cost at about 3½ mills per kilowatt-hour, the burner-upper reactor must figure 7 mills.

The burner-upper is the only type so far tried in actual service (in the *Nautilus*), and her fuel costs are going to be far higher than if diesel oil were used. So it is hard to see how the simplest type of reactor can compete with the conventional plants now running.

But this isn't the whole story. The minute you consider the converter or the breeder, your economics improves. Dr. Zinn believes that a breeder might have fuel costs as low as 0.013 mill per kilowatt-hour. That is, fuel practically for nothing.

There is a double-headed joker: the apparatus to burn uranium is far more expensive than that to burn coal or oil; and the burden of dealing with ashes is a wholly new expense. "How would you like it," Dr. Hafstad once laughed, "if, instead of merely disassembling your engine to clean it out, your entire engine had to be dissolved in nitric acid, and the rebuilding of it had to start with getting a solution of certified chemically pure iron? That is the fuel reprocessing problem!"

All that can be said with certainty is that uranium and plutonium fuels will probably end up by costing about the same as coal, per kilowatt-hour turned out. Thus, no real economic advantage can come from their use, especially since the apparatus necessary will cost more. So we shall have to look elsewhere than in cheapness for the advantages of atomic power. Even if the fuel cost nothing, it accounts for no more than one-fifth of the price of electricity. The rest goes into plant, investment costs, labor, maintenance and the distribution of power to hundreds of thousands of homes.

17. But Uranium Can Win

• • • • • • • • • • •

How, THEN, can atomic power compete, if not on a straight cost basis? The answer is compactness, adaptability, mobility, and its remarkable talent for entering areas where no one could afford to send ordinary fuels.

For there is a joker in the coal picture, too; much more serious and permanent than the growing pains of atomic fuel. Coal is gradually giving out. In America we think of it as inexhaustible; it is far from that, even in the richest coal-producing country in the world. Mines are getting deeper, harder to work; miners are becoming harder to please and more expensive to hire. Machines are taking their place, but machines can't work thin seams economically. So, much of the coal will never be worked at all.

Abroad, coal troubles are still worse. Britain's coal seams are so thin that even hand-mining is failing. Half the world is in coal starvation. Thus, though there is probably coal enough in the ground to last mankind some thousands of years, its price is bound to rise faster and faster as the easy deposits are used up.

With petroleum the situation is far more grave, as reserves are only a fraction of coal potentialities, while demand for "premium" fuels is galloping ahead every year. Gasoline is the finest fuel we have, pound for pound almost twice as concentrated as coal. The machines that use it are light and controllable and inexpensive. Everywhere the world is turning to buses, trucks, airplanes, oil-fired furnaces. They are skimming the cream off the fuel crop.

Nearly all ocean vessels have converted to oil, the railroads are on the way. Not to mention the automobile, whose expanding legions are committed to liquid fuels. Or the military, which has first choice of fuels everywhere and invariably takes the best.

Comparisons today between atomic power costs and conventional power costs are not much good. They may make the atom look pretty expensive now, but before long things might even be reversed. A few years ago AEC got interested in our atomic power future and asked an engineering consultant, Palmer Putnam, to make a study of the world power situation. Mr. Putnam came up with what is probably the first careful long-range survey ever made.

He began by inventing a new unit of energy, which he called "Q." It was equal to 10^{18} B.t.u., that is, a billion billion British thermal units. With this he drew the world power prospects in bold strokes. Q applies to all human activities which use fuel—heating, transportation, communication, electric power. Putnam went back into history and decided that, up to 1860, the world had used a grand total of 7Q units of energy. Reckoning everything up to 1947, he got 12Q. This means an increase so rapid that by 2000 A. D. the total will be at 30Q.

Stated in another way, almost no energy was used up to the nineteenth century, but by 1955 we will be using up stored fuels at the rate of about 20Q per century. Worse, by 2000 A. D. our consumption will have jumped to 100Q per century. In the next 45 years we shall multiply our energy demand by five!

The importance of Q becomes clear when we relate our Q-demand to the Q-supply of fuel. Here Putnam has a surprise for us. Proved oil and gas reserves today, he says, amount to only $\frac{4}{10}$Q, and even if important new discoveries are made the final total is not likely to be more than 8Q. His arithmetic shows that all probable petroleum reserves will be gone by 1975. This might be stretched out somewhat by liquid fuels made from coal.

Total world coal reserves, says Putnam, may be in the neighborhood of 70Q, though economically usable coal amounts to only 6Q. This puts the situation in a really serious light. Literally, there may be coal enough for a long time, but its price will rise on an ever-steepening curve. Obviously, in a decade or two atomic power could begin to compete, even at its present high cost.

Now comes the payoff for which Mr. Putnam was hired. If breeders work, available uranium for them will run at least to 100Q—the equal of all the coal still in the ground. Gordon Dean, former AEC chairman, adds his own optimistic note: if we include all uranium and thorium estimated to be on earth we get the heartening total of 1700Q. H. D. Smyth goes him one better: usable uranium alone will outlast all coal, oil and gas 20 or more to one.

According to this, then, atomic power will be guaranteed for thousands of years, taking over from coal and petroleum as they get scarce, thus holding down the price of power. We should begin to feel the effects within the next 20 years.

A few will always insist that private power interests will try to hold the price up. This argument is not very weighty, in view of the fact that electric power is the *only* commodity that has steadily dropped in price during the past 50 years of inflation. Not altruism but technological advance has been responsible; there is much more of it to come. And those who are still worried about "power company greed" should remember that power profits are rigorously held down by Federal and state commissions. The only thing that is not held down is government experiment at public expense. This can be costly indeed.

What the fault-finders never seem to remember is the extraordinary versatility of American invention. Under the competitive system let prices get out of line and immediately something new turns up. As recently as 1938 we saw coal as our one reliance for the future. Now, atomic power has more than doubled our prospects. What is to prevent still more discoveries? Suppose the hydrogen reaction can be quieted down from a devastating explosion to a tamed workhorse. It is quite conceivable that we might use all the water in the world as a source of fuel.

Dr. Kenneth Pitzer, an atomic consultant who used to be with AEC, said recently in *Chemical and Engineering News* that he thought important work was being done on this very thing, notably at Los Alamos. He doesn't expect results very soon, but who knows? How often in American technology has a discovery been labeled impossible and then come to pass, almost next day!

The hydrogen-fusion reactor would have many advantages besides inexhaustible fuel: higher temperatures (if we could use them), no neutrons to worry about, no bulky moderators, probably far less danger from radiation, and a much easier problem with ashes. A fusion atomic generating plant would really cause a revolution. With limitless hydrogen to draw upon in the oceans, the millennium might indeed be at hand.

Speaking of limitlessness, of course, there is always solar power. Power enough to heat homes can already be obtained direct from the sun. And just lately the Bell Telephone Laboratories have announced a device made of silicon which actually converts the sun's rays into electricity direct. If this method can be made economically sound, need we worry about coal or oil or atoms or Q's?

The only way to stop such an age of limitless energy for all would be to destroy the incentive to reach it. And that, unfortunately, is an objective, not only of communism, but of too many in our own land.

18. Atoms for the Power-Hungry

• • • • • •

It is reasoning like Mr. Putnam's that makes engineering interest in atomic power so keen. Incentive is there with a vengeance. It is this incentive that has spurred AEC and so many private utilities to make studies and do fundamental research in power reactors. The real drive is not profit; it is the fear that we haven't much time left in the golden age of petroleum.

Petroleum is indeed the most important factor in the long-range atomic program. It must be conserved for the automobile and the airplane, helpless without it. Railroads and military vehicles must have it. Natural gas belongs in the home, for heating. The best way to realize this objective is to begin removing oil from electric power stations and the vast merchant marine of the world—substituting atomic power.

Coal will also feel relief. There will be more of it for the already vast chemical industry. The railroads will feel relief, as the thousands of trainloads of coal begin to dwindle.

Atomic power is not likely to be used first in the United States. A much more logical place for the birth of the new industry is in the power-hungry areas of the world, where fuel is now too expensive for general use. Here, small atomic plants can be built and operated successfully, for there is little competition.

England, with her bad coal situation, is chronically power-hungry. Because of her advanced knowledge of nuclear science and her co-operation with the United States in wartime atomic work, she will probably be the first nation in the world to commercialize the power of fission. Actually, atom-generated electricity may be on the British market within a year or two.

Many other nations throughout the world are energy-poor because of an unfavorable fuel supply. Yet none except Canada, France and possibly Russia has begun active work toward building atomic power plants. With her well-advanced nuclear technology the United States has a golden opportunity to pioneer the power field throughout the world.

The most likely development in the near future is that one or more American firms will offer to build reactors for anybody who wants to buy them and who has the fuel for them. Already, North American Aviation have advertised widely that they will build and install a prototype for anyone for ten million dollars. This has been done with the understanding that AEC approves the project and makes fuel available. Now that the law is changed, NAA will forge ahead as a pioneer in atomic power contracting.

Westinghouse is now fully occupied with the Duquesne plant, but when that is done, their huge new atomic factory will be ready to turn out "package" plants for use anywhere. No doubt General Electric and a few others will soon do likewise. The obvious use of these standardized power stations will be to fill the serious gaps in the world power map. The whole of Scandinavia, for instance, is in need of new power sources. Their hydroelectric potential is about used up. Surprisingly, so is Canada's.

Holland has no water power whatever and must import her oil and coal. Neither is cheap. In Australia the situation is interesting. She has no oil but she has coal and has recently discovered rich uranium deposits. U.S. negotiations for fuel material now under way may well include a reciprocal offer to provide atomic plants as soon as they can be designed. Australia is designing one of her own, also.

Internationally minded people are already imagining how much good could be done by bringing compact atomic plants to backward nations. Our efforts to date have too often resulted in pouring money into such countries, loading its docks with refrigerators and washing machines (and Cadillacs), without much thought as to how these American luxuries can be run. A better approach will be to study how a backward people can best use energy.

In India, for example, power is at an extreme low per capita level. With British and American help they have built a steel industry, but the great majority of manufacture is done by primitive methods. The next logical step is to bring them large blocks of electric power to mechanize production and so raise the standard of living generally. The economic co-operation program of the future will surely include atomic power plants as one of the basic necessities. India herself is much excited about atomic power prospects. Her Tata Institute has a well-advanced nuclear program, and there is some uranium in her soil.

All over Asia the problem of modernization is the same. Millions of coolies live without light or good water because their only energy source is their own muscles. Power is needed first; then can come electric lights, small mechanized factories and finally home comforts. Small atomic plants in the cities of Thailand and Cambodia would transform the people amazingly, and start them on developing their rich untouched resources. A conventional plant, with its long supply lines of fuel, would be out of the question in areas like this. Atomic reactors can go anywhere and the fuel could be brought in by mail if necessary.

Latin America, parts of Africa and many sections of Europe offer the same sort of invitation to the atom. Anywhere in the world where civilization is still primitive, there is bound

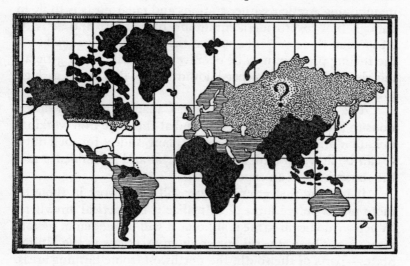

to be a shortage of energy. Power has been too costly by standard methods. The people have done without. Now, with a little outside help they can have it.

Awakened by Rickover's successful atomic submarine the Army has at last begun to figure on its own atomic project—a portable power station capable of being set up anywhere. During the war hundreds of diesel power plants on wheels were used in base camps and on construction jobs. Some were in railroad cars and some in trucks; they could follow the demand anywhere, able to pull up and move in a few hours. It is quite possible to install an atomic power unit of a few thousand kilowatts in a group of vehicles, with the tremendous advantage that the plant would be independent of fuel supply lines. It could go for months on its original charge.

Such rolling stations and probably larger, prefabricated ones, will undoubtedly be seen in remote places such as mining ventures, airfields, oil towns. One of the greatest difficulties in maintaining Arctic weather stations and radar posts is to fly in enough fuel to provide a minimum of comfort and activity. At some of these outposts, such as the Greenland ice cap bases, the fueling problem may be decisive. A typical cost of generating electric power is 4¢ per kilowatt hour—ten times as high as at home.

The same thing is true at the Canadian uranium operations in the northern wilderness and at the huge iron workings in Labrador. A small atomic power plant is ideal for such duty. It can be flown or sledged in piecemeal and assembled under the supervision of an expert or two.

It is likely that atomic power will be at work in these remote places before most of us realize it is practical anywhere. When we do begin to see it at home it will be hidden in remote areas, too. There are still power-hungry sections in the United States—parts of the south, the northwest, some farming areas. It must be remembered, however, that atomic power will not satisfy a market thinly scattered over hundreds of square miles any better than present power does. Distribution costs are the controlling factor there.

American industrialists already see great benefits from atomic energy in factories which normally generate their own power. Here, fuel costs are a major concern. If the breeder is successfully commercialized the great manufacturing plants may be the first to use it. Monsanto, for instance, has been an instigator in the power field because they use enormous blocks of power in chemical processes, often twice as much as a large city. Their enthusiasm is pretty good proof that they see advantages in atomic fuel.

You may also see the atom at work in remote mining areas. The practice has been to transport raw ore many miles to central smelters. Tomorrow, the whole operation, down to refined metal, may be concentrated at the minehead. There is great saving in money and time wherever a material can be handled in one continuous production line. Not to mention the much lighter burden on the rail line that has had to haul out thousands of trainloads of material, most of which is waste.

Applying this idea to a huge operation such as that on the Mesabi iron range in Minnesota, one can imagine moving the smelters from Ohio and Indiana into this northern region. This will cut down the long line of ore boats that ply the Great Lakes to a few carrying the pig iron itself. The saving in bulk transportation will be enormous. Removing much of the air pollution from thickly populated areas should be important, too.

Atomic power is even more adaptable to the production of heat. Many parts of the giant chemical industry use heat in vats and processing machines—in the making of plastics, dyes, cement, basic chemicals, rubber, fertilizer and many more. Most such heat today is supplied by oil-fired boilers or electric resistors; the atomic boiler can take over nearly everything but the making of steel, where actual combustion is needed to control the carbon content of the metal.

The making of aluminum offers an ideal place for atomic power. This industry is one of the largest users of electric power in America. A pot line for reducing aluminum oxide to the pure metal by electrolysis is often a quarter-mile long, using hundreds of thousands of kilowatts. So big are these plants that they must invariably be built close to major sources of power, usually hydroelectric installations like those on the Columbia River. The latest to be started is the fabulous development at Kitimat, British Columbia, where an entire river has been diverted through a mountain tunnel to obtain the high head needed for running the huge turbines. All those millions spent in altering nature could have been saved by an atomic installation thousands of miles nearer civilization.

Aluminum-making begins with bauxite which comes from British Guiana, close to the equator on the Atlantic. Transportation lifelines, even to the United States, are long and vulnerable. Atomic power at the minehead would cut them down to a fraction, devoted to carrying the finished product and nominal amounts of process chemicals. "Atomic power," says Gordon Dean, "will change the industrial and economic geography of the world."

19. Atoms at Sea
• • • • • •

WITH THE *Nautilus* and *Sea Wolf* accomplished facts the Navy is almost certain to go ahead with atomic power afloat. It would not be surprising, in 25 years, to find the United States standardized on atomic naval power. True, there will be much conservatism to be overcome first, but Rickover has thoroughly shaken the old line. General Mitchell's self-sacrifice brought a revolution in military aviation; from the most reactionary we became the most advanced nation in the air. Something of the sort may follow on the sea.

Now that atomic subs are assured, the destroyer would be an ideal next step. The enormous power (50,000 horsepower, or thereabouts) required to obtain speeds of 40 knots, places such severe demands on the destroyer that it is virtually all engine room below decks. Fuel bulks so large that cruising range is small; top-speed operation range is even less. Here, atomic engines will do a wonderful job in cleaning up an engineering anomaly. A 150,000-kilowatt atomic boiler will take up no more space than present boilers; shielding will not consume as much space as old-style fuel. The reactor will contain all the fuel needed.

Greatest advantage of all will be the ship's freedom from

supply vessels. Fissionable materials kept in stock at major naval bases will be sufficient. Refueling and ash-handling time in port will certainly be no longer than the present oil fueling is now.

The work that Rickover's people have already done on the CVR reactor is expected to form the basis for atomic carrier engines when the Navy is ready for them. Lately AEC authorized a new study by a large shipbuilder to bring the main problems to light. The carrier is now the foremost fighting ship of the fleet. Successful experience with the subs should soon lead to atomic carriers—say within ten years.

As for the smaller vessels: if the destroyer can use the atom to advantage so too can a number of more plodding ships such as supply vessels, troopships, cruisers, even escort ships and possibly the brave little seagoing tug. Her long voyages over the great oceans of the world put a severe strain on her fuel capacity. A bucketful of uranium would see her around the world.

One can imagine the Coast Guard making good use of atomic drive, especially in such powerful vessels as icebreakers. As the war threat lengthens our fighting lines into the Arctic, long fuel lines become increasingly serious. The icebreaker that can spend an entire year away from her base will have an important military value.

With this great activity in naval atomic power, merchant marine owners are sure to consider uranium engines for their ships as well. But the problem is somewhat different for them; economy, not military mobility, must be the criterion. It will take a little longer to put the atom into the ocean liner and the freighter.

To the commercial vessel problems of fuel storage, fueling time and cruising range are less important. The best reasons for switching to atomic engines are reduced fire hazard and the reduction of use of precious petroleum reserves.

Norway is at present the most enthusiastic for merchant marine conversion, with the Dutch a close second. In 1951 these two maritime nations joined to build an experimental pile at Kjeller, Norway, for the express purpose of developing engines for ships. Most likely they will be the first to ply the seas with atomic power. Probably not, however, with their hosts of small tramps, which eke out a nomad existence well enough with coal. You will see some of the big steamship lines take it up first; no doubt atomic power will come to be a prime advertising point in luxury travel. There is already much competition from transoceanic air lines, however, and passenger liners are not likely to "atomize" until real savings are in prospect. Economic advantage could come fast, of course, if research keeps on at its present high rate.

There is one possibility worth mentioning: the conversion of big liners to troopships in case of an all-out war in Europe or Asia. It might then be that the western governments would subsidize atomic power in large vessels to obtain the last knot in speed and rapid turn-around time in port. High speed and agility are prime requirements in seagoing troop movements; especially so with an ocean full of atomic subs.

From a design point of view the atomic reactor is very attractive for marine engineering. A basic advantage is that it does not grow in size as the power rating is increased. A football-sized core will produce the energy to run a carrier if the temperature is high enough. Thus a reactor's physical size depends mainly on the area of the surfaces required to transfer the heat. Problems of heat transfer are very tough, and depend upon safe operating temperatures in the structure and cooling medium. Nevertheless, research is turning up better materials every day. By the time atomic power reaches commercial acceptance on the oceans, the reactor for a *Queen Mary* may be only about ten times the size of one for a tug.

20. Atoms Aloft

• • • • • •

In the descending order of probability for atomic power tomorrow, the airplane comes next. Quite early in the game large military aircraft were proposed as an ideal vehicle for atomic engines, because a plane's fuel range is embarrassingly short. Soon after the war the Air Force, in collaboration with AEC, set up a project to explore the possibilities. A number of industrial firms were asked to submit proposals for airframes and atomic propulsion units.

Their task was principally to work out basic designs of reactors and shielding that would be practical in the air. It was a very tough problem indeed, for they were going back to the days of Langley and his steam-driven airplane, which unhappily failed to wrest the honors from the Wrights. The designers were now competing with the world's most compact engines, phenomenally light and easily controlled. Jets weighed even less per horsepower. Against these stiff odds the engineers had to gamble a minimum of some 50 tons of shielding, the weight of the pile and fuel, and add to it the bulk and weight of steam turbines.

Surprisingly, some of the world's foremost aircraft specialists said it could be done, even offered to do it—in very large bombers. They were given contracts to go ahead with the construction of both plane and power plant. The project suffered the same delays and arguments that bedeviled the submarines, and has lagged along on paper for a number of years. As this is written, however, progress is looking up; an additional $30 million has been added to the original $20 million, and a "testing facility" for land-based aircraft units has been started in Idaho. The project is naturally highly classified and little information has been given out. There is probably nowhere near the human zeal behind it that Rickover gave to the *Nautilus*.

According to Colonel W. S. Barksdale of AEC's Reactor Development Division, the turbojet and the ramjet engines are the types most likely to be seen first in an atomic airplane. Both require large volumes of very hot air (now obtained by burning liquid fuel), to be ejected to give thrust. The turbojet compresses its air in a rotary compressor, the ramjet by merely crowding the air that rushes into it in flight. The idea is that atomic fission could supply the heat and the energy to spin the turbine.

The ramjet is especially promising because it has no rotating parts. It is simply a tube of peculiar shape. Fuel burning inside raises the gas pressure and blasts the mixture out of the rear end. Such an engine was used in the infamous buzz bombs that harried London during the war.

Both types of engine burn gasoline simply to produce the high temperature and consequent high jet velocities. Atomic heat might replace the combustion of fuel.

The problem looks staggering but AEC is going ahead with it, so there must be a reasonable chance of making the machine work. No one can tell how long it will be before atomic planes fill the sky. Ten years at the least, probably longer, unless a new war hastens the art. But fly they certainly will, whether they do so efficiently or not. You can well afford to use an inefficient engine, says Dr. R. P. Petersen of AEC, when it takes only a couple of grams of fuel to fly from here to Moscow!

Advantages, again, are with the military craft, which can ignore economy. The outstanding value of the flying atom, Colonel Barksdale points out, is extreme range and the ability to complete a mission, any mission, and then get home regardless of weather or devious routes. Bombing missions today must be planned with extreme care to allow just enough fuel to return to base *by a planned route*. Bad luck in weather or the enemy forcing the plane into a long detour, often end in the loss of plane and crew.

This would not happen with the atom-powered bomber, which could stay in the air almost indefinitely, outwaiting the weather or going around by any route that was safe.

These advantages would be shared only partially by commercial aircraft, which have so many possible landing points that there is always enough fuel to reach them. Unless remarkable improvements in economy can be shown for the atom, nuclear planes are not likely to be seen for a good many years. One minor advantage they will have, it should be noted, is that fuel load will not change in flight. Hence take-offs and landings will be simplified, under conditions of constant load.

There is no hint so far of the actual design of an atomic plane engine. One way it could be done, it seems to me, is to use pure U-235 or plutonium in a small sealed vessel actually placed in the combustion chamber of the jet engine. The vessel would then act as its own heat exchanger, doing away with cooling fluid, pumps and moderator. But extraordinary metals would be required, able to stand incandescent temperatures.

Such metals may be nearer than we think. One of the newest is an alloy of cobalt and nickel that has tested out successfully at 1600 degrees. Steel would run like butter at this temperature. Then, experiments in powder metallurgy promise combinations of metals and ceramics which will stand heats up to 2200 degrees. "Cermets," they are called. Most attractive possibility seems to be molybdenum, with a melting point of 4750 degrees. Today it is useless, for it oxidizes rapidly. But the "moly" experts think they can protect it with silicon. Already it has stood up for hours at 3000 degrees.

Whether these heat-resistant alloys would do for atomic reactors has not been divulged; they might be neutron-stealers, or they might collapse under intense radiation. We can only be sure that scientific research will gradually close in on the goal of suitable materials for whatever duty the atomic age demands.

How can a plane tolerate a 50-ton radiation shield? Most planes can't. But the huge B-47 bomber carries 50 tons of gasoline at take-off, so that there might actually be a saving in weight with atomic engines. A few pounds of uranium would be ample for a B-47.

I believe that the first atom-powered bomber will be announced within the next few years. It will be experimental but will no doubt work. It would be no surprise to find the United States in possession of a Navy and an Air Force with many atomic units within 25 years.

Ralph E. Lapp, a former AEC scientist, thinks that the atomic reactor might bring the dirigible airship back. Millions were spent in these vessels of the air between wars, when gasoline engines were the standard power units. One advantage would be a conspicuous reduction in fire hazard from large cargoes of inflammable fuel. Another, the unvarying weight of the power plant throughout the voyage. In the old ships a serious lightening resulted from burning up the fuel, only partially compensated by water condensed from the engine exhaust. The rest of the weight loss had to be made up by discharging lifting gas, an expensive proposition.

A good many people like to dream about atomic power for guided missiles and space ships. If one is to believe in flying saucers, it is necessary to assume some form of atomic engines. Whether or not the coming guided missiles will use atom propulsion is anybody's guess. The Pentagon is not saying. The case for atomic rockets, however, is rather hopeless, unless brand new principles of physics come to light. For there is an indispensable factor that fission engines can't supply.

A rocket must *push* against something, according to Newton's Third Law of action and reaction. The thing it pushes against is its own fuel as the combustion gases are accelerated and ejected behind. It does not push against the air. Obviously it couldn't in space. Since atomic engines produce only heat they do not impart high velocity to particles of matter in any one direction. Hence, to make an atomic rocket work you would have to load it with some heavy substance which could be speeded up for the sake of the reaction. But then you would be right back where you started.

The beauty of present-day rockets is that their own fuel supplies the heavy substance to be accelerated. Hence it is possible to attain extremely high efficiencies in a vacuum, efficiencies close to 100 per cent. This is more than double the figure for any other known power system.

The ramjet, mentioned earlier, would work out with atomic power *in the atmosphere,* since it depends on ejecting heated air from its nozzle. In space it would not work at all.

There remains the fact that *if* flying saucers are real (a question this book makes no attempt to decide), they must have some power-producing device completely beyond the known laws of physics. Their fantastic ability, often reported, to dart hither and thither, accelerate, turn at top speed, stop, rise and hover, suggests only that their owners know how to circumvent the very Newtonian laws of mass and acceleration which so far have bound us to this earth.

I would be the last person categorically to deny that this couldn't be done, but the first to doubt that it has been done by any scientist on this planet. For, if such advanced propulsion has been worked out by any nation, why are we wasting our time with atomic energy?

21. Atoms on Wheels

● ● ● ● ● ● ● ●

HIGHLY SPECULATIVE, but quite possible, is atomic power on the railroads. No transportation engineer, so far as we know, has yet given serious consideration to it. However, the Department of Physics of the University of Utah has done so, and rather proudly presents a well-organized report on it.

In 1953, their graduate course in Nuclear Technology, under Dr. L. B. Borst, asked the AEC if they might make a railroad study. Dr. Petersen of the Industrial Power Board replied that the government would welcome such a study, and agreed that enough unclassified information was available to make it authentic. Dr. Borst immediately put his students to work on the problem, first obtaining support from the Union Pacific Railroad, General Electric, Westinghouse, General Motors and others expert in the field.

It is significant that these large companies co-operated so readily, for it shows how eager is American industry to explore every phase of the atomic problem.

Noting that the question of an atomic-powered locomotive has already been considered by Schurr and Marshak in their book, *Economic Aspects of Atomic Power*, Borst's group of three students and three staff members writes:

The only real economic incentive for atomic power for rail transportation comes from a possible reduction in fuel costs. This is particularly true of the first few locomotives. At a future date, if atomic units replace diesels, there may be further economies due to the retirement of fueling equipment in the same fashion that diesels have retired extensive watering facilities.

Atomic units will require infrequent refueling, which must be done at an elaborate central facility. This refueling operation can be conducted in conjunction with a planned maintenance program.

After several months' work the group had come up with a complete dossier of computations and designs, which would certainly be of interest to any railroad executive, and can be obtained direct from Dr. Borst. The group's summary and conclusions are briefly stated at the beginning of the report:

An atomic-powered locomotive has been found to be technically feasible. It would be a 7000-horsepower unit having twelve driving axles and a total length of 160 feet.

The reactor would be of the "water boiler" design, 2x3x3 feet, having an output of 30,000 kilowatts of heat in the form of steam at 250 pounds per square inch. Contaminated steam would be used to operate a conventional condensing turbine, the heat being rejected through finned radiators to the atmosphere.

(This means simply that, when the steam has expanded through the turbine and done its work, it will be reduced to water in an air-cooled radiator and returned to the reactor. The act of condensation produces a very good vacuum, which gives the turbine better efficiency. This is standard practice, except that most steam condensers are cooled by water, which would be too bulky here.)

Power transmission through conventional geared generators and traction motors would insure good operating performance. Electric locomotive performance can be achieved because of the overload ability of the reactor. Short-term powers of 9000 to 12,000 horsepower can be attained.

Economic studies are necessarily incomplete in the absence of fuel costs (i.e., the price of U-235). If U-235 costs less than $7 per gram the locomotive could compete with equivalent diesel power under optimum conditions of load and service.

Problems of health and public welfare are considered technically soluble, although the exact arrangements have not been detailed.

Some of the performance notes in the report give a good insight into general reactor operation. For instance, by using the water-boiler type, which generates steam directly around the core of the reactor, Dr. Borst's group obtains automatic safety control, as Dr. Zinn outlined. Automatic load control is also inherent.

The university study takes a thorough look at the economics of the atomic locomotive. By-passing development costs, which AEC would undoubtedly have to finance, it finds that a complete locomotive should cost about double the diesel figure. These extra investment costs would have to be canceled by better fuel economy and higher performance.

Maintenance is a feature that can't be ignored. Like all reactors, the locomotive cannot be opened up for every trivial failure. The group thinks this would be no problem, as practically all reactors to date have solved it. They have been so carefully designed and built and tested that they work without interruption.

High-speed, high-power service is the field expected to show the best gains for atomic-powered locomotives. The new engine will have ample overload ability for steep grades and, as its designers point out, electric locomotive flexibility and smoothness without the cost of electrifying the whole road.

A long guess on the coming of atomic railroading would

be 20 to 30 years. This is longer than for most other applications, in fact, since the advantages are smaller and the development costs pretty high. Then, too, there is the gas turbine to be exploited in this field. The turbine might well be an intermediate step between the diesel and the atomic giant of the rails. Yet who knows? Even the conservative railroader might suddenly jump the intervening steps. It would be no surprise in the atomic age.

And now, what of the auto of tomorrow? Imaginative people, a lot of them journalists, have repeatedly dreamed of the car into whose tank one merely puts an "atomic pill" and then forgets about fuel for good. Two hundred years on one pound of uranium, let us say. The only thing the prophets didn't mention was a name for the gadget. I suggest "atom-auto," conveniently shortened to "tomauto."

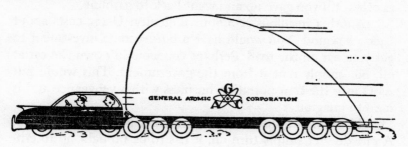

Gasoline has been doing a fine job in the family car for 50 years, and would certainly not yield to the atom without a struggle. It would have about everything on its side, too. First, shielding. Not a scientist is to be found today who will admit that shielding can ever be light in weight, since it is weight itself that provides the resistance to radiation. Thus, our atom-autos are going to be embarrassingly heavy, carrying 50 tons or so of lead or concrete or pig iron to save us from being rayed to death by our engines.

But suppose they do find a weightless shield through a loophole in physics. We are then face to face with inexorable economics. For the chain reaction requires a minimum critical mass of fissionable material. The figure hasn't been divulged but it is a matter of pounds of U-235, much more like tons if it is ordinary uranium.

Anyway, the minimum critical mass would be enough to furnish power for the relatively tiny requirements of a car for decades, maybe 50 years. Thus, when you sold your car for junk it would still have virtually a new engine and its tank would still be "full." Tank and engine would run through dozens of cars. You might, of course, imagine a system in which you bought a mileage interest in a car (which would be as big as a Pullman and have the tires of an earth mover), sold it for scrap and installed the engine in another vehicle and then another, till you gave up and went back to gasoline.

Another insidious economic difficulty: U-235 costs about $4000 a pound. You would have a burdensome investment to get your car on the road. Perhaps you wouldn't own the car at all, but simply rent it from the government. This would put AEC into the transportation business with a vengeance and is hard to imagine.

The atomic auto would be a nuisance in the morning, too. A pile doesn't simply turn on, it has to be brought up to criticality and the chain reaction started with great care. In the presence of experts this takes at least an hour, and is said to be the only moment when a fission reaction is in real danger of getting out of hand. An answer might be, that once started at the factory, the atomic engine would be kept running day and night, as long as you owned the car. . . .

It would be a trifle embarrassing to get into a crash with your atomic car and its 50 tons of shielding. It might mow down a whole block before its accumulated momentum could be absorbed. And if the reactor happened to get smashed it might spread fission products far and wide, making a whole street uninhabitable for weeks.

There's a story about the old Stagg Field pile that tells of a day when some frisky young scientist spilled a container of fission products on the concrete floor. The resulting contamination was so bad that the university decided to close the area altogether. When I visited it ten years after the accident the place was still out of bounds.

Dreamers of atomic autos also like to speculate about houses that are heated by atomic pills. A tiny pellet dropped into the furnace when you buy the place and your heating troubles are over. Well, practically over, except in the fall when you have to have the experts in to start the system up. Most likely they would clear the whole block, because if the reaction got out of hand it might melt and burn down your house, spreading radioactive smoke all over the place. It might be quite a fire, too. That $5000 worth of uranium should be enough to heat the little home for 500 years. Going off all at once. . . .

I do not intend to be facetious about atomic heating. In large blocks, for hundreds of homes joined together, it might work very well—something like the central heating scheme found in the towns on the Mesabi iron range. Nobody has a furnace there; all buy heating steam from a central station through a meter. An atomic community boiler might be very attractive indeed—smokeless, probably not too expensive, efficient.

Atom furnaces in large plants or in big institutions are likely to come into early use because the reactor is so sensitive to demand. It can produce the heat of a match or of a conflagration merely by turning a control knob. There will be no banking of fires on warm days or burning the doors off on cold ones; no unsightly coal pile, no soot on the wash. Such a heating plant could be as ornamental as any school; it could even be built underground.

This is all prophecy, of course, and in detail may be wide of the mark. But you will see developments along these lines, perhaps far more spectacular than can now be imagined. As for the auto and the home, once atomic power has taken the unfair burden from oil and natural gas, the cost of premium fuels should certainly go down.

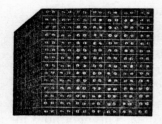

22. Big-Time Power

• • • • • • •

LET US look at the not-too-immediate future when atomic power has taken over a significant part of the energy burden of the country. This will be after the battle in which it has won its place against its formidable adversary, present-day steam-electric power. That battle will have done it good, for it will have brought out every bit of ingenuity the atomic engineer can muster. The result will have been the finest blend of everything that is excellent in the present system and everything that atomic energy can add.

Some of its contributions may shape up like this: atomic power plants will be a good deal more compact. Unlike the conventional steam plant, they will not have to have any particular shape, no huge coal yard or tank farm, no tall stacks with their drifting smoke.

As already mentioned, reactors do not get bigger in proportion to their capacity. Dr. Petersen puts it this way: "In a conventional power plant generating a few hundred megawatts (say 250,000 kilowatts) of electricity, you have a boiler that is perhaps 40 ft. on the side and about 80 ft. high. It is out of this volume that you take heat. The same amount of heat in a reactor is developed in a filing cabinet."

Thus, very large atomic plants will depend for size and

design on their electric generating equipment. Amazing strides are being made in higher steam pressures and temperatures. Thousands of engineers are trying to increase that 25 per cent of the fuel that goes into useful energy, by taking a bigger bite out of available heat. Temperatures of 1500 degrees, and pressures of 3200 pounds per square inch are feasible. This enormous increase in working conditions (many plants still work at 750 degrees and 1000 pounds) will play straight into atomic power's hands. A small, compact reactor delivering furious heat through brand-new metals; turbines built for gigantic stresses, generators that crowd every material to the utmost under high-pressure helium cooling—these are the elements the high-school kids of the future will see when they visit the light company's plant. And it will be in a building that looks more like a library than a power station.

Freedom from coal supply will be a major advance. Some plants today use 500,000 tons a year and, because of the danger of strikes, must keep huge supplies on hand. They must also be near rail or water transportation. Not so the atom plant. So long as it can have a plentiful supply of water for its steam condensers it can be anywhere. In seaboard cities it would not have to occupy premium waterfront sites so that coal barges could tie up at its door.

The atom plant of the future will be clean and moderate in size, though it will care for a whole city. At present, AEC takes a very conservative view of the extent of the "exclusion area" necessary to protect the public from possible radiation hazard. But scientists believe this will not be necessary much longer. Atomic piles are to be inherently safe, as we shall see in the next section. We shall hardly know that they are among us.

Who will own them? This is a question quite as important to the people as the engineering advance. Already there is great pressure on Congress not to allow atomic energy to be socialized.

It is unlikely that the AEC will ever own more than a few pioneer plants. It certainly doesn't want to.

I suppose (says Dr. Petersen) this is the first time in history that a monopoly has spent $12 billion and has tried to get out of a monopolistic position. . . . It seems appropriate that a billion dollars in capital investment (per year) should come from private money rather than from the Bureau of the Budget. This is the game we are playing for. This is the business of peacetime atomic energy.

Dr. Petersen is referring to the strenuous efforts of the commission to sidestep the responsibility of owning the new atomic power business. The commission itself and the overwhelming majority of scientists, engineers, business executives and politicians want the people to have it, which means that it will be developed by private groups in competition with each other.

The presentation of the atomic future to the people, already begun in the new Atomic Energy Act (passed on August 30, 1954) need worry nobody on the score that control of the atom may get into the hands of "private monopolies." Power companies are inherently regional and there is decided competition from city- and government-owned plants. Thus it appears probable that we shall see the largest atomic stations integrated into the over-all plan of tomorrow's cities, many of them municipally owned.

Such cities will be laid out with two distinct advances in design: efficient location of industry, skillful blending-in of rail transportation so that whole areas will not be condemned to exist "on the wrong side of the tracks." There is nothing more absurd about present cities than the persistence of great slums around industrial areas, rail centers and slaughter-house districts. The crux of the problem, really, is the location of energy centers. In our older cities, the industries grew first, dragging the power plants in after them. In our future cities, power will come first, in the proper place, and industry will follow.

I have taken a flyer at designing a city myself, basing it upon well-proved designs of small towns lately built. I call it my "ring city." In it I have established the giant power heart at the center of a circular area, with ample room for all needed auxiliaries such as switching yards and the modest equipment needed for handling fuel.

The whole city is arranged as a series of ever-larger concentric rings, with radial avenues starting at the center. In the first "band" outside the power core are the industries, so close to the source of power that transmission is all underground, and inexpensive. Stringent rules prevent smoke and industrial fumes and wastes. Such as there are must be condensed at the site or carried away through underground ducts into the country. The industrial band is just so wide, ample but limited. Once it is full no more industry can find room. The city is not supposed to grow beyond reasonable size.

In the next band outward comes the commercial community: offices, department stores, professional buildings; restaurants, theaters and parking spaces form the outer fringe of this ring. And in the final annular zone we have the dwellings, the homes being placed on wide, curved streets with numerous parks. Schools and churches are accessible in each community without the interference of main highways or railroads. Beyond this we have the open country, the farms, airports, golf courses, lakes, and a city-owned area large enough to prevent the metropolis expanding indefinitely. Somewhere out here the radial transportation system comes to the surface, branching out to the four points of the compass.

The two principal geometrical features of our ring city are the circle and the radial line. Many of these radii are boulevards, sunk below building level so as to segregate traffic and hold down noise. They cut the town into segments, each of which has its own local stores and services. The narrowing of the wedge as it approaches the center compresses business and industry into a higher building density, with the atomic power supply at the highest density of all. Conversely, this give homes the most land.

Major transportation in the ring city is by tunnel. One large central railroad station serves the whole thing. Water, communications and motor traffic also come in underground, presumably under the main boulevards, with feeders leading off on the way. The main boulevards, however, are *not* trunk highways; if you want to leave the city you dive into a tunnel. Since my city is designed with adequate parking areas, there is never going to be a traffic jam (I hope).

I have laid out my city with provision for ample expansion to a predetermined total of, say, 500,000 people *and no more*. For a long time there will be empty land, waiting for development, but it is carefully zoned. If you want to start a business, build a factory or erect a home, you will have to do it in the area appropriate to it.

A dream like this, of course, ignores a great many practical matters such as topography, regional industrial demands, and the apparently insurmountable urge of chambers of commerce to expand and expand. However, it is a goal to strive for. Based upon a hitherto unrealized standard of energy per capita made possible by the atom, it should be entirely practical to build such a city.

Now, what about the enemy bomb? Is not the circular city the best of all possible targets? There is no question but that it is. *If* an enemy can reach it. But any city, round or square or scattered, is a fine target. Thus, if it were decided that aerial attack was likely, the atomic plant and the major industries could be built undergound. With uranium power there is nothing to prevent this. A reactor can run underground indefinitely and unauthorized persons would never know where it was.

DANGER

RADIATION

23. How Safe Is Atomic Power?
• • • • • • • • • • • •

IF THE United States is to be dotted over with atomic power plants a good many people are going to be uneasy at first, wondering how safe they are. Too many will confuse the benign power station with the bomb. The reactor, they will say, is really a bomb, held in check by main strength.

Too much has been written about the "fallout" from the hydrogen explosions of 1954 for people to be comfortable about the atom. Innocent parties were injured by atomic ash at great distances from the explosion. Fallout even occurred several thousand miles away, on the continent itself. The public has a right to know the risks.

The partly informed will also argue that the government should not abandon the extreme caution of its exclusion areas and the special safety provisions of such things as General Electric's giant steel sphere.

Let us analyze the matter objectively. An atomic reactor is not a bomb. Completely out of control it could not explode. Only those on the inside know how extraordinarily difficult it is to concentrate fissionable material and hold it together long enough to produce a detonation. To do so means design of the

135

highest ingenuity, superpure fuel, special "tampers," the last word in neutron concentration.

We are not told in any detail how these factors have been achieved, but we do know that even the most concentrated power pile is not the proper apparatus to achieve them.

When you interpose controls in a chain reaction you use the fuel far more effectively but you use it slowly. Even if the controls fail—as we shall see they did at Chalk River—the structure of the machine defeats any fast buildup of explosive energy. Metals melt and run down but they do not zoom through the air at bullet speed. AEC's Dr. Hafstad puts it, in effect, that power reactors conserve the heat and throw the neutrons away, while bombs utilize the neutrons and throw the heat away.

The reactor can, of course, produce heat enormously fast —fast enough to reach some 10,000 degrees if allowed to do so. But that is stone cold beside the tens of millions of degrees within the bomb. If sodium cooling is used, there can also be a nasty explosive fire. In neither case, however, are forces met with which cannot be contained within a good strong building. The principal danger in the atomic plant is similar to that in steam plants of today—an explosion of steam.

For centuries steam boilers exploded and killed, till elaborate inspection laws intervened. Today one does not hear of very many; virtually none in big central stations.

In a press interview in Washington Dr. Hafstad summed up the risk of atomic explosion in response to a journalist's question:

It takes a lot of hard work to make an atom bomb. You have to have everything just right to get a good explosion. Reactors are not designed to be good bombs. . . . So, if you have a malfunction you are not going to get an atomic bomb explosion.

How Safe Is Atomic Power?

The main danger is the release of radioactive gases which dribble out into the atmosphere and over the countryside. Assuming that your controls went bad, (the reactor) wouldn't heat up and vaporize in large quantities. . . . In general we talk in terms of *meltdowns* rather than explosions. . . . You try to guard against all possible uncertainties and you put in lots of (safety) apparatus. As you gain confidence you begin to eliminate these things. I think this is the stage we are going through now. The things that we are now making are probably overdesigned and with more experience we can cut the costs considerably, without sacrificing a high degree of safety.

The one major accident to a large reactor so far, occurred because this very matter of refining overelaborate controls was under experiment. It happened in Canada's huge 30,000-kilowatt reactor at Chalk River in the northern Ontario wilderness, on Friday afternoon, December 12, 1952. A low-power run was in progress, in a study of pile behavior at start-up. Certain controls had been deliberately disconnected, and the cooling water which ran through jackets around the uranium had been cut down on about ten per cent of the 176 fuel rods.

As we have seen, start-up is the critical moment in a reactor. With control rods in place, not enough neutrons survive to maintain the chain reaction. If the rods are pulled out just a little, the neutron flux builds up till the neutron survival factor, k, exactly equals 1.000. But allow the controls to relax ever so little, and k becomes greater than one—perhaps only 1.001. At this stage the machine has reached a geometric increase in fissions per second. The more neutrons that are liberated, the faster new ones are set free. In an amazingly short time the power production can go from nothing to a staggering quantity. Now, normal control mechanisms anticipate this, instantly throttling the neutron flux till its *k-factor* returns to 1.000. Here, at any working power level, it is forced to remain by supersensitive interlocked absorption rods "floating" in the pile. At appreciable power the control is firm, and little danger exists of a runaway.

NRX, the great pile at Chalk River, was feeling its way along in this critical zero-power-plus region. Suddenly, controls still on duty ganged up in a fantastic concatenation of failures. There was a mighty surge of power and in a fraction of a second a *hundred million watts* of heat flashed through the complex of uranium rods, fusing them and their aluminum jackets, spewing vaporized fuel and radioactive fission products into the cooling water and a stream of cooling air which lay beyond.

Only the few rods were destroyed which had had reduced cooling—about 20 of them. But these were enough to jeopardize the whole structure. There could not be an explosion but if the pile melted and burst its shielding, the whole plant could be saturated with deadly radiation.

"We had taken a calculated risk," Fred Gilbert, chief of the Reactor Division explained later, his Scotch smile rueful. "But our calculations weren't quite good enough. Seven different things went wrong simultaneously—some human, some mechanical. It was a million-to-one gamble that no such thing could happen. But it did."

Automatically, the emergency sirens wailed over the plant, and personnel in every building dashed to shut windows and doors, cut off telephone calls to leave the lines free. Staring out into the winter dusk, they saw Dr. Cipriani, chief of Radiation Hazard Control, hurrying down the street fastening on his respiration mask. They knew this was no drill.

A few minutes later the sirens blasted again—the evacuation signal. Cipriani's men had found that a cloud of radioactive air, blown up NRX's stack, had produced fallout enough to upset many delicate experiments if it were tracked around by normal traffic. Thus, though there was no radiation danger to personnel most of the 1700 in the little atomic city were sent home, leaving the scientists and executives and the regular NRX crew to deal with the disaster.

They had their hands full. At the instant the power surge had sent off the alarms, emergency controls were operated manually, and at the same time the pile's central tank, or calandria, was emptied of the 5000 gallons of heavy water used as a moderator. This cut off the chain reaction in about two minutes. The primary disaster was over. But not the emergency. Uranium is pyrophoric. If it is filled with fission products, as these rods were after five years of service, it can get hot enough to burst into flame, creating a furious fire that cannot be stopped. Obviously, it was essential to keep the cooling water flowing through the machine. But to do so meant to pour it through the ruptured tubes into the basement.

Half a dozen department heads, the director and others, huddled in the NRX control room, confronted with this dilemma. "Keep that cooling water going!" the director ordered tersely. "Let it flow into the basement!"

They could hear the crashing of the water as it tumbled through the damaged calandria unhindered, submerging and contaminating everything in its path. They knew only too well that they had let themselves in for a cleanup job that might be impossible.

For days the water poured down, submerging piping, equipment, instruments. By Monday morning a million gallons sloshed through the basement, loaded with 10,000 curies of radioactive wastes—seven times the total activity of all the radium produced since the Curies discovered it. The situation grew more serious by the minute, as contamination seeped into cracks and crannies, permeated even the concrete itself.

The pile was out of danger but now the building had to

be saved. Doggedly, the directors decided on an emergency pipeline to a disposal area over a mile away. Luckily there was not much snow, and though the ground was frozen hard, welders and pipefitters were able to lay the pipe, shield it where it crossed the streets, insulate it against freezing, and get it into service in nine days. By Christmas Eve the worst was over. Chalk River faced a new year of cleaning up, a scrubbing job without precedent. Not only must the men work for months in an atmosphere of constant danger from radiation; they must finally dig down into the vitals of the pile itself, a feat that reactor experts believed impossible.

24. Skill Beats the Atom

• • • • • • • • • • • •

THE CRUX of the problem was human safety. A person may be exposed to fairly strong radiation for a short time, or to weak rays for a longer one, without harm. But he must not *accumulate* more than his body can safely absorb. Radiation destroys body cells; the danger point comes when the number of cells destroyed is too great for the body to replace. As we shall see in detail later, the unit of total exposure is the *roentgen*. Conservatively, the Chalk River medical people set the safe limit at 0.3 roentgens per week. At this level a man might go on exposing himself indefinitely with safety. Or, he might acquire as much as five roentgens in a short time, provided he received no further radiation for at least four months.

Thus, from the start, the Canadians' most vexing problem was manpower. There were simply not enough "man-roentgens" among the skilled operators of NRX, to carry through the decontamination job. Immediately the management rounded up every available pair of hands and willing back in the plant, to do the menial work of pushing mops and handling scrub brushes. They took clerks, accountants, guards, janitors, chauffeurs, most of whom had never seen the inside of the reactor building before. These people were pushed through fast, to make way for the skilled artisans who must do the dismantling of contaminated machinery. Many an amateur scrubber got his full five-roentgen dose in a few days and thankfully went back to his routine job.

For skilled help Chalk River sent out a call to all Canadian armed forces and beyond to the AEC in the United States. The response was overwhelming. Units of skilled radiation-control men from her own Army and Navy flocked in. From below the border came specialists from the American atomic submarine project, from General Electric's Knolls Laboratory, from the new Westinghouse atomic factory and from Electric Boat; from the Navy's Radiological Defense Laboratory. Friendship, curiosity and an eagerness to help write this new chapter of atomic history brought them to Chalk River—scientists, skilled artisans, sailors in squads and platoons.

A vast amount of plain scrubbing and hosing off had to be done to get the insidious fission products out of their hiding places. But it was no common charwoman's work here. Before a scrubber could be risked inside the building he must be rehearsed with models and photographs in every move he was to make, so as to avoid the loss of a minute's precious exposure time. Cipriani's men, of course, were continuously monitoring every inch of the place, mapping the danger spots and working out safe routes and forbidden areas.

No person might enter the building without a complete outfit of white coveralls, hard shoes and rubbers and the infamous respirator mask. In a mask a man sweated till his goggles fogged; his voice was reduced to a meaningless mumble; there was always the lurking fear that the mask might be leaking, letting in the dangerous contaminated dust that had settled everywhere. And masks did leak, in spite of the best inspection. At one time 80 men were temporarily excluded because they

had exceeded their radiation allowance by breathing through faulty masks.

Everyone wore a film badge and dosimeter and these were checked for exposure at the end of each tour of duty. All hands had record cards, to show how much "safety time" they had used up and how much they still had left.

Trickiest job in the cleanup was the dismantling of "hot" apparatus that had pocketed strong radioactivity. An ingenious camera came up from Knolls Laboratory that greatly speeded up the finding of the danger areas. It was a lead-encased adaptation of the century-old pinhole camera, carrying two films, one behind the other. Focused on a suspected machine, the front film simply took a picture of the object in ordinary light, while the one behind pictured only the spots of high radiation. Superimposed one on the other after development, the pair instantly located danger areas. Geiger counters would have done the job, but in days instead of minutes.

The high-level workers who attacked these danger spots were forced to undergo a special routine. They were dressed in clean underwear, coveralls, plastic suits, gloves and masks; sometimes clean outdoor air was supplied to the suits through pipes to prevent dust from working its way in. Coming off the job after minutes of exposure, they went straight to the showers and were thoroughly washed down, suits and all. Next, they were stripped by special undressers, to avoid the danger of smearing themselves with contamination, and were showered again, then monitored. If any trace of activity remained on a man's body, back into the shower he went, and the routine was repeated till the counters remained silent in contact with the subject's skin from head to foot.

Chalk River's worst manpower problem was among the supervisors, for there were too few of them to permit expenditure of irreplacable exposure time. Early in the game the U.S.

Atomic Energy Commission realized the problem and sent to Chalk River a complete television outfit, with cameras built for remote control. From then on the work of directing the cleanup was carried on at a distance, away from all radiation, the supervisors issuing orders over a loudspeaker system while watching every move on the TV screen.

Gradually, as Canadian and American experts puffed side by side into the summer of 1953, the gigantic scrubbing job was done. In some places contamination had gone so deep that several inches of concrete surface had to be chipped away and replaced. Every foot of the NRX building had been flushed, scoured, flushed again, vacuum cleaned, tested and painted. Meanwhile, behind massive shields, the highest skilled of all were gingerly lifting out the scrambled wreckage inside the pile, till the bare and empty calandria tank was exposed.

For weeks specialists had been studying this two and one-half-ton aluminum cylinder from high up in the roof. Its removal was to be the crucial part of the whole affair, for it was the largest radioactive object ever handled by human hand. Its radiation field measured so high that anyone coming within 50 feet of it would be overexposed immediately.

An elaborate plan for lifting out the calandria had been worked out and rehearsed on a small model, then rehearsed again at full scale, using a dummy tank filled with sand. The idea was to lift the calandria clear, then lower it into a canvas bag held open on a wooden sled. Drawstrings would then close the bag to confine any possible loose dust, and the sled would be hauled away to the disposal areas by tractor, and heaped with sand.

Seventy men, including many Americans, reported for the job. Every man knew his part by heart; a dozen stand-ins stood ready "in the wings" to take over if an emergency arose. Photographers were spotted behind shields, ready to pop out and snap the scene as it moved along. High at one side of the room the crane operator waited behind a broad lead shield. Expected radiation intensity had been mapped over the calandria's entire journey, so that the Hazard men knew exactly what each actor's exposure would be.

From the control room the announcer's voice suddenly droned out the opening command: "Step number one: attach hook to lifting device and align hook for lifting!" There was a prolonged grunt from the crane as the hook glided down into the depths of the pile. There was a long moment of suspense, then a sigh of relief as the stained but innocent-looking tank slowly rose into view and hung in midair.

'Health men take survey readings!" Out from behind their shields they hurried with their counters, made quick checks of the radiation, then dashed back again.

"Four minutes for photographs!" Now the camera crew was out, clicking their shutters, scurrying back to safety.

Precisely on schedule the weird game was played. The calandria, which could kill any man that might blunder too close, swung out into the room, hesitated and sank smoothly into the waiting bag. The draw-ropes were pulled tight and the sled let down from a standing position to the floor. Then came the snag. A long steel pin which had held the lowering cables on the sled, could not be withdrawn.

"Stand-by crew! Stand-by crew! Move out and try to relieve that pin!" The announcer was keeping his voice as calm as possible.

Experts, scientists mostly, who had been dreading just such a moment, worked their way in behind the mass of the pile, avoiding the radiation field as best they could. Making quick forays from there, they managed to get hold of the ropes controlling the sled. Then, in a masterpiece of unplanned action with the men on the pin, they managed to maneuver the jammed bar of steel out of its socket. The crisis was over almost before it started.

"Rope cutters, cut all trailing ropes!" boomed the announcer as the tractor picked up the tow rope of the sled. Axes flashed briefly and the last tie was gone. The procession began to move. Out through the deserted plant it went like some strange funeral cortege; supervisors in cars ahead, monitor men well behind, the tractor driver sitting stolidly in the shadow of a massive lead plate rigged to screen him from the dangerous load he was towing.

It had taken just 35 minutes to do this job that atomic experts had feared was hopeless.

Today, in 1955, NRX is back in service. Experience gained by the accident has so improved the controls that the reactor can turn out one-third more power than before. And the entire atomic world has breathed a sigh of relief. Here was an unknown limitation that many feared could not be overcome: once a pile had gone wrong, it would be too dangerous to repair. This, we know now, is not so. Safety procedures will make it possible to deal with radiation on the loose as effectively as with any other mechanical accident. Enrico Fermi was right when he said, half humorously, that we need more bombs that don't go off and more piles that do. What the art needed, just at this point, was a reactor that misbehaved.

We know, too, that radiation accidents in atomic research or atomic power, can be met without hazard to the community, and with reasonable safety to the men involved. At Chalk River, even though the pile wrecked itself so badly that it had to be taken completely apart, no one damaged even a little finger. There is no reason why another accident of similar kind, in some future power plant, should not be handled as well.

With one exception: if we are to have atomic locomotives

and planes, what may happen in a crash? Dr. Borst's report remarks: "If numbers of atomic locomotives are in operation one will inevitably be wrecked. . . . The first and all-important operation which must be carried out with absolute assurance is to shut the reactor off. Safety devices must be devised so that under any imaginable situation the main reactor will be stopped."

Borst suggests an ingenious arrangement of control rods in which inertia would cause them to drop into place upon any sudden jar or change of direction of the locomotive—something not very different from the air brakes which automatically set if any supply hose breaks.

The safety of the public, if an atomic locomotive or airplane crashed, would, in the long run, depend on whether the container holding the uranium and fission products remained unbroken. This is not so difficult to insure as it may seem. The massive shield around the unit could be made integral with it. If it were catapulted out of the vehicle, even if it were dropped out of the skies, it would hold together and at least there would be no radioactive death sprayed around.

Hardly anyone living near tomorrow's airports would be happy if he thought that 50-ton lumps of concrete and steel were likely to rain down. It is a good reason for doubting whether the skies will be filled with atomic planes very soon.

25. An Embarrassment of Ashes

• • • • • • • • •

IN SOME ways the worst problem of the atomic age may turn out to be the drab matter of ash handling and disposal.

When a uranium or plutonium nucleus undergoes fission it breaks into two nearly equal pieces, which are driven away from the explosion with the energy of 200 million electron volts. (An electron volt is the energy one electron acquires by "dropping" through an electric field of one volt). These fission fragments are large, however, and are soon stopped by the fuel material or moderator, like an enraged bull charging into a dense crowd.

Most of the fragments remain embedded in the fuel. Since they are more stable than the original material they cannot be split again by neutrons but only rendered radioactive, if they are not so already. Their principal harm is that they steal neutrons from the chain reaction, thus "poisoning" it and eventually stopping it. This is readily shown by the fact that as a pile continues to operate its control rods must be withdrawn more and more to maintain a given power level. Fission products inside have run away with the job of control.

"Ash" handling in atomic power plants will be a mean

job because these radioactive products are deadly to humans and because they cannot be removed from the fuel pieces without chemically dissolving them out. Thus, a very intricate technical job has to be done behind many tons of sealed concrete walls.

The radioactivity of the calandria at Chalk River measured about 5000 curies—more than three times the output of the world's entire radium supply. A human being could tolerate such radiation for a few seconds but no longer. Many of the fission products are violently active, so much so that they are lethal in quantities as small as $\frac{1}{400,000,000}$ of a pound. The unit called the "curie," it should be noted, measures the number of radioactive particles that are thrown out by a gram of radium in one second:—no mean number, indeed. All other radiation *quantity* is based on this standard.

The fission products are not composed merely of two elements, each half the weight of uranium. There are literally hundreds of isotopes in the lot, variations on as many as 40 different elements from the middle of the atomic scale. All are constantly changing by decay, settling down to stable forms or going on to further activity. Some of this activity is very strong, especially the gamma radiation (similar to X-rays), which can penetrate feet of lead or steel and miles of air. Barium and xenon are most often mentioned as fission products but there is everything from zinc and arsenic on up through bromine, strontium, zirconium, cadmium, tin, iodine and lanthanum and the rare earths.

The worst of it is that the chemistry of these contaminants changes with the element. No one process will eliminate them all at the same time and still leave behind the valuable uranium and plutonium. This is the primary problem that confronts the atomic power industry; the secondary one is the disposal of the poisons once they are separated.

An Embarrassment of Ashes

At this stage of the international game the handling of fission products is so vital to the nation's weapons program that only the most vague information is released on it. The successful operation of the plutonium "factory" at Hanford, for instance, depends upon how completely the newly made fuel can be purified and extracted and how much of the remaining U-238 can be recovered for rerunning. Naturally, nothing is said about the details that might aid the Russians in a similarly vexing situation.

Fission product handling opens the fascinating new field of "hot chemistry," bringing with it a new kind of chemist and chemical engineer. They will have three jobs: recovery of useful fuel, disposal of wastes and the utilization of fission products in industry. Nearly all of it will have to be done by remote handling—a brand new art.

Conducting intricate chemical processes at a distance was never done until the Hanford reactors went into service in 1944. So urgent was the need for producing plutonium that the necessary handling techniques and chemical steps were set up without much preliminary research. Actually, the giant plants in Washington were built on the basis of tests made with micro-quantities of the materials, then modified only if they failed. No attempt was made then to reach a final solution for the problem of the ashes.

In general, the uranium slugs that are ready for cleanup are pushed through the back face of the piles into a canal filled with 30 feet of water. Here they simply wait, perhaps for weeks or months, till the short half-life radiation subsides. Then they are moved on some form of underwater truck to the recovery plants.

Dr. Zinn, who is very much involved in this phase of reactor work, says whimsically that "a detailed examination of this question (of reactor economics) becomes a jumble of neutrons, dollar signs and HNO_3." Presumably the nitric acid is for dissolving the uranium slugs that come from the pile. We can guess that the first step is to turn all the solid products into nitrates.

Any high-school chemistry student knows that the compounds of the various elements can be separated from one another chemically because they all behave slightly differently in solution. Some dissolve in one thing, some in another, some precipitate out, some recombine into still other compounds. This is the heart of inorganic chemistry. Hats should be off to the chemists who worked out the process, however. To do it all at a distance without direct contact, and be sure of it, was a great scientific achievement.

From AEC statements it is evident that even the simple removal of uranium and plutonium from some 40 contaminants is an involved process running through many reactions. Since a lot of the isotopes are short-lived, and transmute to other elements during separation, an even wider variety must be dealt with. The cleanup job taxes the chemist's resources to the utmost.

He has the help of very ingenious mechanical engineers, of course, who have invented amazing gadgets to conduct the long separation cycle sight unseen. Little has been said of this most vital part of atomic power production. It is known to be slow work. An operation that would be completed in one minute normally, might take an hour at Hanford.

When the valuable fuel elements have been recovered there remains an enormous bulk of "soup"—liquid solutions of the various radioactive salts, most of them with half-lives of years or centuries. Depending upon whether the radiation is high or low the stuff is diluted or concentrated, then dumped into huge vats deep in the ground. Here, for the time being, the government is content to leave it, making sure that there are no leaks which would allow the dangerous liquid to contaminate the ground water. The Hanford reservation is big enough to care for waste storage for many years to come.

In the atomic power field there will be no such simple solution to the problem. Large exclusion areas around plants are not contemplated; dangerous wastes definitely cannot be stored in thickly populated areas. Nor could the chemical processing be done too close to crowded centers.

The chances are that AEC will inherit the nasty problem of the fission products for its own, perhaps permanently. By stringent regulation of atomic power plants, they will control every bit of ash that is turned out, and are likely to be the ones who will have to act as "ash men." Government trucks of special design can be imagined calling at regular intervals, checking in new fuel, loading on the old. They will then disappear to some remote processing reservation, unload their cargo and take on rejuvenated fuel for another delivery. Perhaps we will arrange with Canada for such a reservation in the northern wilderness. Or we may stake out wild areas in our own northwest. It will certainly have to be on marginal land where the public will never come.

Careful studies are already being made of the matter; the main problem is to lock the fission products into some medium from which they can never escape. Water is very doubtful; it can leak or evaporate. Clays have been suggested as good binders. Concrete may prove to be better. Whatever it is, this time civilization has created a kind of garbage that cannot be reabsorbed into the life cycle. For radiation, even in very low concentrations, cannot be tolerated by humanity as a steady diet.

The question of costs is a knotty one, too. An atomic power industry already at an economic disadvantage from expensive fuels and plants cannot bear much more in the way of ash handling costs. Nor can the government become a permanent partner without upsetting the delicate balance between free enterprise and socialism.

The ash-handling dilemma might be relieved somewhat if it were possible to include a reprocessing plant with every power station, thus doing away with long-distance bulk transportation of dangerous materials. Such a plant might turn out very concentrated isotopes to be moved to the disposal area in radiation-proof lead "pigs," as is done now with medical isotopes. Some fraction of this product would undoubtedly go into medicine and industry and never have to be stored at all.

Yet another possibility is that the concentrated isotopes themselves might be put into special plants to give up their energy and turn it into power. About ten per cent of the energy of fission is said to come from the radiation of the fission products. In the aggregate, this is large—enough to be worth saving if some method can be invented to convert it to heat. If such a conversion plant were incorporated in the main power station it would improve efficiency and get rid of a most embarrassing problem.

There is still another way to deal with fission products: to make the fuel in the reactor a liquid, to circulate it outside the reactor and process it continuously. This is the principle of the "homogeneous" reactor, on which AEC has done a great deal of experimenting. If the same liquid that provides the energy also does the cooling, a very efficient combination results.

One still has the headache of disposal, but much of the intermediate nuisance of dissolving solid fuel by remote control is avoided. The ashes in liquid form collect, drop by drop as the cycle functions, and are stored in "delay tanks," where some of the worst radioactivity spends itself. The liquid is then concentrated to reduce bulk and is shipped to disposal stations.

The homogeneous reactor (HRE) has had little publicity.

For it to work commercially there must be a cheap, rapid method of chemical separation automatically controlled behind massive shielding. The AEC has not admitted that such a process has been discovered. Dr. Hafstad, however, has explained that the homogeneous reactor has very important advantages besides reprocessing ability. There is no trouble from solid fuel rods collapsing, no shutdown for changing fuel; the whole thing, being a liquid process, fits into well-known engineering routines. But he points out one serious shortcoming:

"It is between fuel elements which disintegrate, and containing vessels which dissolve." Any solution of uranium compounds, used at a high temperature, is viciously corrosive.

The best compromise for the present seems to be to make the fuel last as long as possible before having to be processed: that is, what is called "long burnup." Dr. Petersen expresses the hope that burnups may some day be stretched so far that it will be possible to throw the residue away without any processing at all. Some part of the deadly fission products will, of course, be left, but not all.

Paradoxically, the vexing problem of government control of fuel (on account of the bomb), may make the ash-disposal problem simpler. It will be AEC's headache to solve both at once, thus leaving industry free to concentrate on generating cheap power. At this stage it is impossible to tell, for a great deal depends on what kind of reactors prove to be most popular. Burner-upper, stretcher-outer or breeder, solid fuel or liquid, air, water or liquid-metal cooling; a few large reactors or many small ones; piles that consume their own ash or spew out vast quantities of deadly isotopes. Or perhaps hydrogen-fusion machines that avoid most of these problems at one stroke—who can tell?

Truly, there are many complications ahead in the atomic age.

26. International Atom
• • • • • • • • • • •

DURING WORLD WAR I, when Sir Ernest Rutherford was working intensely to transmute nitrogen into oxygen, he received a summons to a government research conference. He refused to interrupt his work. "If I have indeed split the atom," he wrote an official, "it is more important than your war."

We know how vital his split atom has become since in military affairs. But what Sir Ernest meant, more likely, was the atom's extraordinary potential in the peaceful affairs of men. He looked ahead even then, perhaps, to the day of atomic power such as we have seen opening in these present chapters.

Entirely apart from its military significance, atomic energy has become a major force in international relations, and a basis upon which an entirely new approach can be made to restoring friendship throughout the world.

President Eisenhower understood this when he made his plea before the United Nations for a nonmilitary atomic bank. So hungry are the nations of the earth for energy that they are bound to gravitate toward those which have already begun the development of the atom as a constructive force.

The United States, Canada and England are today in the forefront of the atomic art, and since they are traditionally peaceloving and not aggressors, their know-how in nuclear science gives them a powerful diplomatic implement in the conclaves of nations. Actually the English-speaking nations (soon to include Australia) have the opportunity today to start a new era of peace and plenty, based upon the good that natural forces can do for man.

Paramount in this great move toward peace is speed. Without question, the western nations are in an atomic race with the Soviets—the Russians have announced it themselves. The two opposing ideologies are already competing with each other for the laurels of peaceful atomic power. "It is of paramount importance to our international relationships generally," says Walter Bedell Smith, former Undersecretary of State, "that the United States maintain and improve its leadership in atomic energy development. It would be especially damaging if the Soviet Union were to precede us."

This puts the matter somewhat on a par with the Olympic games. It is a contest, ostensibly for scientific supremacy, but really for the respect and support of a large part of the free world. If we are to win we shall need all the speed and effectiveness we can muster.

As I have pointed out, our opening move is to help the backward nations obtain the benefits of atomic energy at the earliest possible moment. By the time this book is in print this will have been implemented by a liberalized Atomic Energy Act, authorizing the United States to share part of its now-secret information, principally with our friends in Great Britain and Canada.

The next move will be to stabilize the world situation in uranium. We have seen that Belgium and Canada are the only western nations possessing rich deposits of pitchblende ore, with Australia a potential third. As things stand now, we would be largely dependent upon them for atomic fuel. No matter how friendly a foreign nation may be, dependence upon it for a basic raw material is not economically desirable. It would be better if the United States had its own plentiful supply of the essential fuel of the new industry. Otherwise, supply lines will remain too long, too costly and too vulnerable in case of war.

Fully aware of this the AEC is making tremendous efforts to develop our domestic uranium supply. By devising effective new methods of refining low-grade ores and by promoting an intensive search for high-grade materials, they propose eventually to make this country self-sufficient in everything that atomic energy needs.

A fascinating sidelight of uranium geography is the opening of unexplored lands at the ends of the earth. Uranium, the geologists remind us, is everywhere. Rich deposits are as likely to be hidden in the Antarctic, in Greenland or Labrador, as in Central Europe or the African jungles. So far as we know, no one has yet searched for uranium in any of the Arctic areas, yet it is sure to be there, very likely in important quantities. Mineral exploration in high latitudes would be extremely difficult, but a tremendous challenge to that pioneering spirit which has given the world its great discoveries.

No way is known today to prospect or mine economically beneath the ice. Yet it could be that the bomb itself holds the key, as Eddie Rickenbacker once suggested. Properly placed atomic charges certainly would melt a lot of frozen wastes. Let the competitors for peaceful atomic laurels consider the world's marginal lands. There is no reason why vast riches in tomorrow's fuel should not be found in them.

The most important of all phases of international atomic energy is the free interchange of scientists and scientific information, without respect to national boundaries. Dr. Ralph Lapp points out that it is doubtful if the United States could have achieved the bomb without the help of a number of brilliant foreign minds. We are moving ahead toward atomic power today with the aid of these men and others like them. The mightiest force of all for peace will be the even distribution of scientific and engineering brains throughout the free world.

Science cannot live in a strait jacket. Freedom means everything. Freedom to work when, where and how the spirit moves; above all, freedom to discuss findings and to draw upon a general fund of basic knowledge kept strictly up to date. Through war necessity the English-speaking nations have from the beginning turned their backs on this basic scientific principle. Nothing could be worse for peaceful atomic energy than secrecy. We have today a concentration of technical knowledge in isolated camps, to the embarrassment and disadvantage of men who should be playing on the same team. Our enemies have drawn upon this knowledge too generously while stupid officials looked the other way.

With stolen help from us and with her own considerable genius, Russia has made progress almost equal to our own. It may be comforting to believe that science cannot flourish under Soviet regimentation. But is it true? Many thoughtful people who have studied the matter report that their atomic energy program is in good shape. Though the party line seems to have interfered with biology and psychology and agriculture, it certainly has not curtailed physics and engineering. Two Russians, Fleroz and Petrazhak, discovered the fission of uranium simultaneously with Hahn, Strassmann and Meitner in Germany. No country has a more brilliant physicist than Kapitza, who taught in England until 1935. Mendelyeev, the author of the periodic table of the elements, was a Russian. Soviet players have recently beaten the world at chess.

We have little cause to be complacent about our competitor in nuclear engineering. We should assume that the Soviets are as good as we are on the atomic front.

Earnest efforts are being made in Europe to bring together all the competent men in nuclear work. Under the title of the European Council for Nuclear Research, set up by UNESCO, ten nations have joined at Geneva to build a great modern research laboratory. Neither the U.S. nor Great Britain yet belongs, but both are giving their support. Very likely the organization will play a vital part in Eisenhower's plan to build a world atomic bank.

Indeed, the atom has unlocked forces greater than its own. It has meant the rebirth of all science. It has given the world many new avenues of exploration and more—a new *pace*. For our side let it be said that science thrives in the atmosphere that stifles war—the atmosphere of freedom.

PART TWO
· · · · ·
The Magic of
Radiation

		[b]Xe 121 40m	[b]Xe122 20h	[b]Xe123 1.7h P 72.8	Xe 124 0.096	[a]Xe125 18h K r.05-24, A6	Xe 126 0.090	[b]Xe 79e IT 37 r.10
54	Xe 131.3 (54)							
53	I 126.91 (53)	[c]I 120 ~30m P 4.0 r	[c]I 121 1.6h P 1.1,—	[c]I 122 3.6m P 3.3	[c]I 123 13h K.o r.159	[a]I 124 4.04 K,P 2.20 r.60, 1.7 2.0, .7	[a]I 125 60d K, L r.035

I. Radioisotopes

• • • • • •

THE AMERICAN people came out of the war with a weary sigh, a guilt complex and a world-shaking discovery. Everywhere the public prints shouted about the new atomic bomb, the cataclysmic power of fission, the end of the human race. Scientists joined the clamor. Some announced that they were ashamed of their achievement in opening Pandora's box. Some packed up and gratefully returned to the seclusion of their universities, free of the demand to kill.

But a handful of quiet men at Oak Ridge went on experimenting with an obscure side effect of bomb-making: the ability of the atomic pile to create new atoms that nature cannot make. Early in 1946, a converted war-research reactor began turning out a trickle of radioisotopes that were to be of profound importance to medicine, agriculture and industry.

In "those days" science recognized 92 natural elements and two man-made ones, neptunium and plutonium. A considerable number of variations on them were already known, mostly stable, some the artificial products of earlier research with the cyclotron. Now, suddenly, the neutron atmosphere available in the piles could add many hundreds of new isotopes to the list.

For reasons still not entirely understood, nature has limited the variety possible to each element. As we have seen, each has, by definition, a certain number of protons of positive charge, maintaining an equal number of electrons of negative charge. Some of the electrons account for an element's chemical properties.

Each atom is rounded out by a quantity of neutrons, and nature tolerates a variation in this quantity, thus allowing a number of isotopes to each element. The isotopes of an element have slightly different atomic weights and different degrees of radioactivity, or none at all. Otherwise they are identical. Nature has apparently not bothered to make most of the possible radioisotopes, or else did so at the beginning and lost them all.

Thus we have sodium with a single natural isotope, gold with only one, iron with four, mercury with seven and tin with ten. The reason there are no more is that only these configurations are stable enough to survive. An analogy would be a triangle of billiard balls pushed close together on a table. The three will lie there indefinitely. A fourth can be added on top; the pile will still remain, though its stability is less. But we cannot add a fifth; there is no place for it to rest.

By adding neutrons the number of natural isotopes of an element can be increased. The great majority of these are partially unstable, that is, radioactive. By throwing off alpha or beta particles or gamma rays, or combinations of them, they consolidate themselves into stable isotopes or transmute into isotopes of near-by elements, either stable or still radioactive. The heavy elements do this spontaneously, without man's tinkering. Uranium, for example, becomes lead after 14 generations, of which radium is the sixth.

A salient feature in all this is that every radioisotope has a specific *rate* of decay. When half of the atoms in any sample of an element have undergone change, one half-life is said to have passed. During the next half-life period, half of what remains will have changed, and so on. The activity of the sample, therefore, fades away according to a definite descending curve. After ten half-lives a radioisotope's activity is down to about one-tenth of one per cent. That is, it produces only $\frac{1}{1000}$ as many disintegrations per second as it did when we first considered it. There is no known way to alter the half-life period. It is a fundamental constant of nature.

The great discovery quietly made during the bomb rush was that man could fashion hundreds of radioisotopes at will, and that these would be of transcendent value in scientific research because they could be located in a much larger quantity of the parent element by radiation counters.

Adding neutrons to a small sample of sodium or gold or phosphorus meant that you could find it wherever it went, and so identify what part the element played in a vast number of chemical reactions.

The discovery was not as clear-cut as it appears, but a matter of new mass production methods. For years the cyclotrons had been making microscopic quantities of radioisotopes at huge expense. Now, with neutron densities of a million million per square centimeter per second (an average level in an atomic pile), any element placed in their path would be quickly enriched in one or more radioactive forms. The great importance of pile-made isotopes was that they could be made in considerable quantities at very little expense.

The pile at Oak Ridge held the honors in isotope-making for some years, long enough to establish it as a world-wide business from which AEC, and therefore the taxpayer, derives considerable income. Today there are other manufacturing centers. The giant at Brookhaven is by far the largest; there are also isotope producers at Argonne. Some isotopes are made, also, in the materials-testing reactor at Arco, Idaho. North American Aviation in California is the first private group to build and operate a "neutron source": it has turned out two, one of which is helping the oil industry in petroleum research at Livermore, California. The probability is that we shall soon see these isotope-makers spotted all over the land.

Since half-lives range all the way from millionths of a second to billions of years, production and use cannot be entirely standardized. Some of the most important isotopes have unfortunately short life spans and must be put to work at once. At the University of California, scientists had to snatch treated samples from the cyclotron and carry them at a dead run to the laboratories. Brookhaven's first real business came in supply-

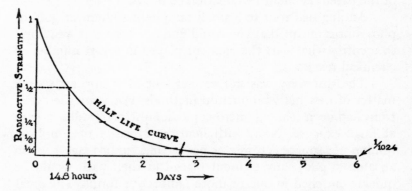

ing radiosodium to the Harvard Medical School. Taken from the pile at 6 A. M., shipments were flown to Boston by private plane and put to use before noon.

Radiosodium (usually in salt) has a half-life of 14.8 hours, which makes it safe to administer to patients both for treatment and diagnosis. Radiogold is half gone in three days, potassium and copper in half a day. All of these require special transportation to get them on the job in time. Cobalt-60, on the other hand, halves its radiation in five years or more, so that it can be packed and shipped at leisure.

From the beginning, AEC's isotope department worked

diligently to set up transportation methods that would be as fast as possible. Today, most of the critical isotopes go by plane; if the distance is too great they cannot be supplied at all. When the business is fully organized, every large medical laboratory and hospital will have its own isotope-making pile, supplying whatever doctors and scientists need, on demand.

2. Better than Microscopes

· · · · · · · · · ·

THE WONDERFUL usefulness of the radioisotopes comes from the fact that they can be detected a few atoms at a time. Even the electron microscope with its hundreds of thousands of magnifications cannot "see" such small amounts of matter. Gordon Dean points out that as little as a billionth of a billionth of a gram of some isotopes can be detected. He says that $\frac{1}{100,000}$ of a gram of radiocarbon can be accurately measured when spread through the tissues of 20,000 guinea pigs.

Thus in medicine, agriculture and industry we have a means of tracing the progress of any element or compound vastly more sensitive than anything available before. This "tracer" technique is now used in thousands of laboratories all over the world. It leads to understanding bodily processes formerly a mystery; it indicates what chemicals are important in agriculture; it gives industry a new tool for analyzing the quality of materials and products and for controlling many processes.

Detection is done by picking up the radioactive rays on Geiger counters or photographic plates. The Geiger counter is a sealed glass tube filled with gas, with a small wire running down the middle of a metal cylinder. When a hurtling particle or ray from an isotope shoots through the tube the gas momentarily becomes conducting; if a battery is connected across the tube a pulse of current flows. Amplified by vacuum tubes this can be heard in ear phones or seen on a meter dial. More elaborate instruments count and add up the number of impulses per minute, and so indicate in curies the strength of the radioactive source.

A still more sensitive device is the scintillation counter in which entering rays cause a tiny flash of light in a sodium iodide crystal. A photomultiplier "looks" at the flash, amplifies it into a detectable current. Your luminous-dial watch is a crude counter. Held directly to the eye at night the distinct flashes of the exploding atoms can be seen.

Radioisotope research has increased our knowledge of the human body enormously since the war. Physiologists did not understand the details of the blood's circulation or what effect blood pressure has on the distribution of the fluid. They did not know just what part sodium chloride played in circulation or why a salt famine is so dangerous in afflictions like sunstroke.

Radiosodium has helped find the answer. By injecting a sterile solution of it into a vein, the progress of the chemical can be followed with a counter. It is now known that within 60 seconds of the time salt is swallowed it will appear in perspiration on the skin. It is known, too, that in the condition called edema, or dropsy, salt passes through the blood vessel walls too fast, luring water with it into the tissues. Conventional cures sought to drain off the water. Modern therapy seeks to slow up salt migration.

Radioiron has played a similar role in understanding anemia. Injected into animals it shows the rate at which red blood cells are made in the bone marrow. This may point to new ways to treat the malady.

A great deal of work is being done on body metabolism with the help of radiocarbon. It is an intricate study, involving the complex organic chemistry of cells. At the end of the road lies a better understanding of the fundamental processes of life.

Great strides are being made today in the control of heart disease. There is an elaborate research at Harvard, for instance, using a "radioactive duck." The poor duck is fed a vitamin-deficient diet, greased, then made to flounder in a tank of water, taking violent exercise. The bird is killed and its heart dissected and searched for radioactive sugars, proteins and fats, compounded from radiocarbon in its last meal. This is not a sadistic game; the duck goes to a painless death not knowing it has shown the importance of certain dietary components to the vigor of the heart muscle.

In another laboratory a rat, sealed into a maze of glass tubes, breathes carefully sterilized air, while feeding on a radiocarbon-tagged diet. Its respiration rate and the amount of active carbon dioxide in the exhaled air indicate the effectiveness of the food. Energy-giving fats have never successfully been injected intravenously. These studies hope to turn up the reason why and correct it.

A wonderfully intricate University of Chicago experiment uses radiocarbon to explain the mysterious value of digitalis as a heart stimulant. Radiation is introduced into the drug by growing foxglove plants in radiocarbon dioxide, extracting the chemical and administering it to animals. Dissection of the heart muscle shows where the medication ended up, and how it got there.

At the University of California the metabolism of cattle is traced with radiocarbon.

The many isotope-aided researches into the basic principles of living cells are of more fundamental importance to the human race. The biologist has now become a physicist as well. Since the body is composed of living cells which are constantly renewed with compounds of hydrogen, oxygen, carbon and certain other elements, the point of attack is at the birth and death of the cell. The work is in a sense done backward, by learning what destroys the cell or keeps it from multiplying. It is from this work that an understanding of cancer is expected. The disease is a malfunction of the cell's growth process.

Cell damage by radiation is also a matter of great consequence. All cells, and everything else, are composed of complicated chains of atoms bound together into compounds. The speeding particles of radiation cause changes in these molecules by ionization. That is, they knock off electrons here and there, producing ions, or charged fragments. The fragments recombine but often not in their original forms. It is as if you tore a letter to pieces, then reassembled it haphazardly. The new molecules destroy the functional balance of the organ they are in and create cells which die or become, occasionally, uncontrolled monsters.

By tagging cell molecules with radioactive tracers, in amounts too small to cause serious ionization, it is hoped to learn what kinds of monsters result from massive radiation and why their abnormal behavior wrecks the delicate system.

In particular, the giant protein molecules are under scrutiny—enzymes, for instance, which promote many thousands of biochemical processes such as metabolism, muscular activity and the control of growth. Although these tiny actors in the body have been studied for more than a century, radioisotopes are the first tool which allows the biochemist to manipulate the actual atomic building blocks of the body.

There are thousands of different cells, but all with the same basic structure: an outer membrane of jelly-like protoplasm, surrounding a dense mass called the nucleus. All of it is made up of giant molecules called proteins, built up by bodily alchemy from smaller units, the amino acids. It is the proteins, apparently, that sustain the most damage from radiation; most vulnerable of all are the amino acids in the nucleus itself.

To make sure of a concerted drive on this great problem, AEC has financed a series of studies, in its own laboratories and in those of many colleges and universities. Here are some of the findings:

(From Argonne): Cell materials most susceptible to radiation are certain enzymes which include a sulfur and hydrogen link easily attacked by oxygen.

(From the University of California): Radiation slows up the proper formation of nucleic acid even in parts of the body remote from the point exposed to damage.

(From Columbia University): By studying the long, very large nerve cells of the giant squid, it is possible to understand how the cell membrane holds together and keeps the cell contents from escaping. At M.I.T. graduate students drive to Woods Hole, Massachusetts, in the night, pick up newly caught squid from special fishermen and bring them back on ice, ready for the day's work.

(From Los Alamos): Frogs, given a lethal dose of radiation, can be kept alive for months by refrigerating them. Chilling may prove to be a promising method of permitting damaged cells to repair themselves.

These are brief samplings of the enormous drive the life sciences are making to gain new knowledge through the use of tracers. While the findings are far too technical for us here, some general conclusions can be appreciated. The blood cells seem to be most critically in balance, for instance, along with the bone marrow and endocrine glands. Necessary body chemicals such as vitamin C, cholesterol, glycogen, etc., are also delicately balanced. Female sex hormones seem to have a powerful restorative effect on bodily processes thrown out of adjustment. Why? It may take years and tens of thousands of experiments to find out.

Along with structural studies of the body, in countless biochemical laboratories, goes the use of radioactive tracers to discover the parts played by trace metals. At M.I.T., for example, radioiron and radiozinc are under investigation. Two hundred student volunteers were injected with the iron isotope, and proved that the body needs only minute amounts of the metal for blood hemoglobin, for it knows how to conserve it. The conclusion is interesting: in the national blood-donation program great care must be taken to bring back the proper iron level. The body can make blood but it can't make iron. The Brookhaven Laboratory finds, too, that iron is essential in much larger quantities than supposed, for the muscles.

Zinc, at M.I.T., proved to be a vital ingredient in white blood cells. Chromium, Harvard scientists report, is a tiny but important constituent of many types of cell.

The list might go on indefinitely. When its achievements are finally assembled, if ever they are, medical science may know how to keep the human body in perfect condition or to restore any function that has failed. This may not be of much satisfaction to us now, but one can at least cheer himself, when he "feels bad," with the comforting thought that his body does pretty well, considering its amazing complexity. An atomic powerhouse, by comparison, would look like a plain sheet of paper. The sufferer can also reassure himself with the thought that the body, 99 times in 100, can take care of itself when something goes wrong.

In radiobiology we have a magnificent demonstration of the intense search for new knowledge. No tool of modern times has been more versatile or more helpful to the fighters on the far frontiers than the radioisotope.

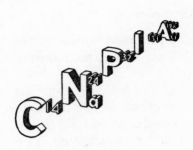

3. Isotopes versus Disease

• • • • • • • • • • •

IF IT is hard for us to see why such painstaking work by so many people is important to our everyday world of living and dying, a potent answer is given by Dr. Vannevar Bush, one of the greatest research geniuses of our time. In his book, *Science, The Endless Frontier*, he says:

Basic research is performed without thought of practical ends. It results in general knowledge and understanding of nature and its laws. The general knowledge provides the means of answering a large number of important practical problems, though it may not give a complete scientific answer to any one of them. . . .

One of the peculiarities of basic science is the variety of paths which lead to productive advance. Many of the most important discoveries have come as a result of experiments undertaken with very different purposes in mind.

Basic research leads to new knowledge. It provides scientific capital. It creates the fund from which the practical applications of knowledge must be drawn.

We should now look briefly at a few of the advances that radioactive materials have brought in medicine. Since basic research in radiobiology and its application to suffering humanity constantly overlap, often running side by side in the same laboratory or clinic, radioactive treatments today are still largely experimental. Nothing is finally proved; doctors will admit only that the new techniques are promising. What seems to an impatient public to be stuffy conservatism is in reality a reasonable caution where human life is concerned. Only harm can come from pursuing new methods too fast.

Just before the war it was found that radioiodine could be made in small quantities in the giant cyclotron at Berkeley, California. Specialists in thyroid diseases—hyperthyroidism, toxic goiter, cancer of the thyroid—immediately realized that here might be a treatment more powerful than surgery, then the only hope. The thyroid gland has such a greediness for iodine that it takes 500 to 1000 times as much of the available bodily supply as any other organ.

The isotope was tried and the famous "atomic cocktail" made medical history. Remarkable results were at once apparent. Overactive and diseased thyroids took up even more iodine than normal ones, and in so doing provided themselves with tiny X-ray treatments. The gland's activity could be cut down simply by drinking a glass of "medicine." Goiter and hyperthyroidism could be cured entirely. Only in the most stubborn cases was surgery still necessary.

The action of radioiodine was simple. At the very seat of the trouble its radiations knocked out thyroid cells and lowered the level of the gland's activity.

Even a few thyroid cancer cases could be helped. But the treatment was expensive. Cyclotron-made iodine-131 in sufficient quantity could easily cost as much as $3000.

Today, radioiodine can be obtained from Oak Ridge so cheaply that it has become the standard drug for thyroid cases. A course of treatment can be had for $100 or less. Hundreds of people who have been run ragged by a boisterous gland that kept them in a constant state of nerves may perhaps need no more than a few "atomic cocktails" and the hospitalization that goes with them. Sometimes a person merely needs to visit the outpatient clinic. A worker in North American Aviation's atomic department one day began throwing Geiger counter needles off scale. The health officer was much worried till the man told him he was taking radioiodine thyroid treatments every week. He was "hot" enough to be mistaken for a radiation leak in the pile. Actually, most such patients show radioactivity like this. Their husbands or wives are advised not to sleep with them while in this condition, though the level of activity is well below the dangerous point.

Control of thyroid activity by a simple drug by mouth has led to an important advance in heart therapy. By cutting down the gland's functioning in sufferers from the fatal angina pectoris, startling relief is often possible. There are even a few cures reported. Many angina victims who were bedridden have actually been put on their feet again; some have been able to go back to their jobs. Radiation of the gland with iodine-131 slows body metabolism and reduces its owner to a placid, nonexcitable existence, with far less load on his heart. This is the kind of small miracle that we can expect to see repeated over and over as radiation techniques are developed.

Here's another: Dr. Charles Dunham of AEC's Biology and Medicine Division, describes a new method for easing the discomfort of people who are bedridden for a long time:

Bedridden persons sometimes have poor circulation in legs and feet, with a risk of blood clots forming. If radiosodium is injected into the bloodstream, a Geiger counter will show how fast blood is reaching the right foot compared with the left. If an artery is blocked, a Geiger counter may help locate the site of obstruction by revealing where blood flow is shut off.

Thus, a drink of almost tasteless salt and water can often relieve suffering for which there was little relief before. Once the trouble is located it is relatively easy to remedy.

There is an isotopic method, developed recently by young Dr. Bertram Selverstone at Harvard Medical, which not only alleviates suffering but saves many lives: the use of radiophosphorus for locating tumors of the brain. These terrible malignancies are often so deeply hidden that even X-rays cannot find them, and they grow to the point where surgery is helpless to eradicate them. But Dr. Selverstone and his associates, Drs. Robinson and Sweet, discovered that brain tumors have a strong attraction for phosphorus—many times that even of the bones.

The patient suspected of having a brain tumor is given an injection of a radiophosphate solution, then allowed to wait a day. The skull is then opened and a very fine, needle-like probe, carrying the tube of a special Geiger counter, is gently inserted, exploring the outer margins of the brain. A nurse watches the radiation count and announces it. When the probe comes near the diseased tissue there is a dramatic rise in response, by 100 times or more, and the surgeons know they have located their objective. Further probing during the operation defines the limits of the tumor much more accurately than mere observation could do. Many hundreds of successful operations have been done in the last five years.

Radiophosphorus, however, is a "beta-emitter." Beta particles cannot travel outward through the bone of the skull, hence the doctors cannot map tumors in advance from outside. A great deal of work has been done on gamma-ray emitters which do penetrate bone and an iodine-base dye, called "RDIF" has been found and successfully used. Another is radiopotassium; still another, a radioiodine-human serum combination said to be the best of all. Each requires elaborate preparation and skillful interpretation, while radiophosphorus is simple and quick.

The list of medical and surgical innovations lengthens every year. There are now few hospitals where some form of radiotherapy is not used. Radiostrontium, for instance, is proving useful in treating small lesions and benign tumors in sensitive areas like the eye. It is also effective in the control of postoperative infection. The isotope is fixed at the tip of a small hand applicator on which there is a thick plastic disk to protect the doctor's hand. The isotope is brought close to the troubled area for a carefully measured time. Since strontium-90 is a beta-emitter of rather low energy the rays do not penetrate deeply and can only be used on the surface.

Applicators are made using isotopes emitting all three types of radiation. Alpha-producers can only be used in direct contact, as alpha particles can penetrate only a few cell diameters—a few thousandths of a millimeter. Betas go several millimeters and gammas can penetrate the whole body. The latter are used for very deep therapy.

Scientists recently made an important advance at Argonne in the use of the sugar, dextran, as a volume expander for blood in transfusions. Tagging with carbon-14 showed that dextran closely duplicates the action of natural blood plasma, and that it can be used as a substitute. In disaster emergencies, when blood plasma is in top demand for counteracting shock, natural supplies often run short. If dextran proves to have no serious shortcomings an almost unlimited supply of it can be provided by the fermentation of sucrose. Commercial Solvents Corporation, working with Argonne, is already developing the technique.

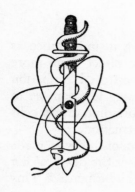

4. Main Target: Cancer

• • • • • • • • •

THE GREATEST drive in experimental medicine today is upon cancer, with the help of radiation. Cancer teams all over the world have stepped up the attack with a vigor quite like that which produced the bomb. In hundreds of big hospitals research teams work directly with cancer specialists and patients. As new knowledge is gained it is tested on animals and, if the new methods are sound, they are quickly tried on human beings.

AEC, realizing its central role in the cancer fight, gives every possible assistance in the drive. Not only does the commission furnish radioisotopes at less than cost, but also contracts with hundreds of university and industrial laboratories for special researches. In addition, it has financed cancer research hospitals at the University of Chicago, Oak Ridge, Los Alamos and Brookhaven. If any proof be needed that the atomic bomb work has yielded real benefits to humanity, the millions now being poured into cancer research by our bomb-makers should give it.

Surgery is still the main hope in the treatment of most

deep-seated cancers, but radiation is rising in importance as technicians refine the beams and learn to direct them more accurately on the malignant tissues to be destroyed. Radiation works by killing the cancer cells, while doing less damage to surrounding healthy ones. Nature helps somewhat; cancer cells are more susceptible to ionization and destruction.

Radium was the original cancer weapon of this type, made so by the tireless efforts of Mme. Curie after the death of her husband. But it is frighteningly dangerous and expensive. Tiny capsules of the metal must be implanted close to the cancerous growth. High-energy alphas and gammas then do the work of destruction. But, since the radiation continues for nearly 1600 years before it is half gone, the capsule must be removed at once after treatment.

Early in the century X-rays began to compete with radium in radiation therapy. They required no surgery; dosage was more controllable. It was found that the higher the energy of the rays the greater was their effectiveness, since they seemed to do less damage on their way through the body to the site of the trouble. However, it is only recently that million-electron-volt X-rays have been available, and then only by using gigantic machines filling whole rooms. The largest hospitals alone could afford them.

A great advance was made during the war with the Van de Graaff electrostatic generator or "lightning machine," originally invented by Dr. Robert Van de Graaff at M.I.T. This is one of the simplest of the atom smashers; by bombarding a metallic target it can generate X-rays of several million volts, in a beautifully defined beam. The machine today is many times smaller than the older X-ray apparatus. Many cancer hospitals are buying them.

At best, the use of radiation for deep therapy is dangerous and is seriously curtailed by the tolerance of the surrounding tissues. Often this limitation prevents treatment powerful enough to destroy the cancerous material. Some years ago Norwegian doctors devised the scheme of strapping the patient to a rotating chair and slowly revolving him in such a way that the cancer remained on the axis of the radiation beam. Like a lighthouse in reverse, this produced high concentration at the focus but only momentary exposure of outlying tissue.

These rotating machines are now used everywhere, with improvements which allow the rays to be focused with great precision by means of lead screens and movable blocks. The human topography is mapped carefully in advance and automatic controls may be used to interrupt the beam as it passes through vital organs.

Early in radioisotope production it was found that radio-cobalt (60) produced almost the same alpha and gamma rays as radium. Cobalt is not a plentiful element but it is thousands of times cheaper than radium. It is also a tractable metal that looks and behaves much like iron; it can be cast, drawn or machined into any desired shape. A standard item from the Brookhaven pile is a tiny gold-plated pellet of cobalt about the size of a match head. The gold is used to prevent oxidization. These pellets are treated in the pile to produce a high radiation level and shipped to hospitals everywhere, to replace costly radium. Production cost does not go much beyond $5, and they last for several years.

Cobalt-60 is "the poor man's radium," and will eventually make genuine radium unnecessary. With a half-life of five-odd years it must be used fairly promptly. It is no plaything, and can easily cause death if carelessly handled. We can thank the Canadians for producing the first high-intensity cobalt-60 in their NRX. Until very recently this pile had the highest neutron density in the world.

A short time ago cesium-137 was proposed as a substitute

for cobalt, since it is found in abundance in fission products from plutonium-making reactors. It has six times the half-life of cobalt and would come ready-made as one of the ashes from the piles, thus being somewhat cheaper, if chemical separation were not too complicated. Its radiation is substantially the same as cobalt and radium.

Another very recent discovery in radiation therapy is that electron beams in the 20- to 40-million-volt range have the property of plunging through an intervening thickness of tissue, then losing their energy to the diseased area, confining their damage almost entirely to it. Electron-beam therapy opens a new territory of experiment, using a variety of atom smashers such as the betatron, synchrotron and Van de Graaff machine. Forty million electron volts is only light duty for these giants, some of which have already reached into the billion-volt range.

The linear accelerator is a relatively simple atomic gun. Essentially, it consists of a series of short copper pipes lined up so that particles boiled off a hot filament will shoot through them in a straight line. By intricate electronic means, using the klystron tube, famous in radar, electrons are given successive kicks as they pass through the tubes, till they finally emerge, going nearly as fast as light.

The linear accelerator was invented by Dr. William Hansen at Stanford University. He also helped the extraordinary Varian brothers to invent the klystron, technically known as a cavity resonator. A giant accelerator, just being finished at Stanford, is 200 feet long and fills a large building. It will work in the billion-volt range. Medical machines, however, designed for a mild 40 million volts, are only six feet long or so. Stanford has equipped its own hospital in San Francisco with cancer-treating accelerators and is supplying others to the Michael Reese Hospital and the Argonne Cancer Research center in

Chicago.

Workers with electron therapy believe that this is one of the most promising new weapons in the cancer battle. It may even give them a means of reaching the now inaccessible cancers of the lungs and liver.

Perhaps the most advanced institution in America specializing in cancer radiation therapy is the Argonne establishment on the campus of Chicago University. It costs the U.S. taxpayer about a million dollars a year, but he is getting his money's worth. The hospital not only uses all of the devices mentioned but is concentrating on radioisotope therapy of many kinds.

Three floors of the hospital are underground, where three levels of cellars reach down into massive concrete vaults where "hot" chemicals are stored. One radiation specialist has charge down here, maintaining the many types of activated chemicals used by the doctors far above in the wards. A kind of super-pharmacist, he keeps daily records of the potency of each isotope. When a prescription is sent down, say, for 100 millicuries of radiogold, he dilutes a portion of the stock chemical to bring it to that count at the time it will actually be used on the patient. This involves Geiger measurements and computations based on the half-life and quantity of the solution used. When the small vial of material is ready it goes up to the doctor in a little lead pot, with its life history written on an attached card.

All over the building you find radiation counters blinking away. Electronic controls are everywhere. Many rooms and vaults have special interlocks so that only the holder of the right key can get into them. The locks become unworkable when there is dangerous radiation inside. Everyone wears film badges and carries pocket dosimeters and is checked daily for the amount of radiation he has picked up. We shall see later what is done if he gets too much.

A row of glass-lined tanks occupies one sub-basement and all sewage from radioactive sources is held there until it "cools" enough to be safely dumped into the city lines. If radiation remains too high the contents can be pumped into tank trucks and hauled 25 miles to the Argonne Laboratory, where there is room for long-term storage and final disposal. The hospital air, of course, is completely conditioned and monitored. It is

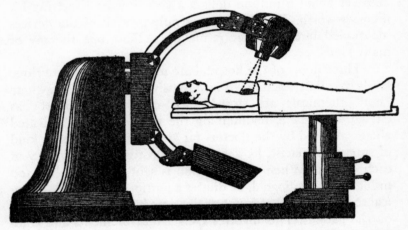

scrubbed clean of any radioactive dust before discharge into the city atmosphere.

Way down at the bottom in a series of heavily shielded rooms the various experiments with cobalt-60 are going on. In one, a constant level of radiation is used to determine the long-range effect on colonies of mice and guinea pigs. This is part of a basic study of hereditary modifications produced by changes in genes and chromosomes.

In another room at this level is Argonne's version of the rotating treatment device. Here the table remains stationary with the patient on it while the cobalt source travels slowly around a vertical ring surrounding the table. This is one of the few instruments in the world shielded with uranium rather than lead. The cobalt is embedded in a 950-pound uranium cylinder, equivalent to 3300 pounds of lead. It can do the work of $36 million worth of radium.

On this same floor, devoted to high-energy radiation, there is also a large Van de Graaff machine and a 50-million-volt linear accelerator. Patients, of course, are alone in the treatment rooms during irradiation. Monitors and scientists watch them and big banks of instruments from safe positions outside of several feet of lead glass, or a glass tank filled with zinc bromide solution. The controls bristle with safety interlocks, alarms, intensity meters. The dosage pattern, worked out by the doctors to an absolute second-by-second schedule in advance, is set up on servo-mechanisms that automatically carry it through precisely. So far as modern technology can insure it, the cancer battle is fought with complete efficiency.

Argonne Hospital, however, guarantees nothing. As Dr. Lester Skaggs of the staff puts it, "The hospital is to be regarded as a research hospital in every sense of the word and is not to be used for the treatment of common diseases or even of cancer by methods already established." There are beds, on an upper floor, for only 56 patients, who are chosen by the participating doctors from hopeless or near-hopeless cases, purely for their research value. A sick person does not apply; he is invited by the university, which operates the institution under contract to AEC.

One phase of the Argonne work is to develop rigid routines for handling dangerous radiation. Utmost care, for example, is taken to avoid spreading radioactivity beyond the patient. Everything and everybody—bed linen, bed pans, food, dishes, air, personnel and even visitors—is constantly monitored for contamination. A "health physics" group spends all its time monitoring, testing, cleaning up.

On the top floor is a completely air-conditioned animal farm stocked with rats, mice, rabbits, and guinea pigs. Many of these animals are supplied to research men on the lower floors, while many more are treated or operated on in a clinic which parallels the human clinic below.

Thus we have today's frontier of cancer research and experimental treatment. It is not unique. It is only typical of the determined campaign that all science is making against the insidious disease.

5. Cancer:
Where Do We Stand?
• • • • • • • • • •

THE MOST cruel overstatement that can be made today is that cancer "can be cured." It is too soon for any such claim. Though the fight has been waged for nearly a century, the true nature of the malady is not yet known; deliberately executed cures are not possible. Responsible doctors claim only that some malignancies can be "arrested" or "prevented."

This is not unduly pessimistic. Tremendous advances have been made and many more are just over the horizon. One could make the risky prophecy that the cancer menace will be controlled within the lifetime of adults now living. Science, once it trains its guns on a problem, ultimately succeeds by gathering enough knowledge to correct nature's mistakes or indifferences. And there is no medical problem in the world attracting so much research brains today.

An approach of great promise is the search for chemical compounds or elements that have an affinity for some one organ of the body, as iodine does for the thyroid. More than 100 chemicals that damage cancer in rats have been found. A project at Ohio State University, for instance, has discovered that 18 kinds of dye containing sulfur show "selective uptake" in tumor tissue, being about five times as rapidly absorbed by it as by normal tissue. This selectivity should make it possible both to locate and treat malignancies with the help of radioactive isotopes of these materials. The method is not as simple as it sounds, however. Many otherwise useful substances are poisons; others have too long half-lives to be permitted inside the body.

At the Sloane-Kettering Institute in New York, antibodies such as those used for immunization against common diseases have been discovered that will seek out a specific organ, perhaps the kidney. They can be made radioactive. Another antibody seems to trace down a malignancy wherever it is. A vast amount of work remains, though, before these substances will be safe and predictable in their effect.

The practical value of these discoveries is closely dependent on basic research in biology, and must wait until the real nature of cancer is understood. One theory is gaining ground: that cancer starts with the overproduction of the giant protein molecules inside the cell nucleus. These are the molecules that are just on the borderline between lifeless matter and living cells. Radiation seems to be deadly to them. Why? A genuine victory awaits the answer.

It was Dr. John Lawrence, brother of Dr. E. O. Lawrence of cyclotron fame, who first used radiotherapy against cancer. He and his associates discovered that radiophosphorus definitely slowed up polycythemia, a rare affliction of the blood, and always fatal in spite of X-ray treatment. But *internal* radiation seemed to control it. This began in 1938. Today radiophosphorus is the preferred treatment for the disease; hundreds have been helped by it.

Lawrence had poor luck with other types of cancer, except

for the much more common leukemia, in which the white blood corpuscles run wild. The phosphorus isotope is of value here though it does not prolong life. It does, however, greatly ease pain and swelling. Leukemia of the lymphatic system responds better. Many people have lived on with it for years, by means of radiotherapy.

Dr. Lawrence also pioneered radioiodine work, but found the response of thyroid cancer poor. It was the surrounding healthy tissue that snatched up the drug, not the diseased part. There has been one important success, however. If cancerous bits of thyroid tissue wander away through the body, radio-iodine will definitely seek them out and in many cases destroy them.

Quite a different approach to cancer has been tried by Dr. Robert S. Stone of the University of California Medical School, who has attempted to blast cancer cells to death with a beam of neutrons. Preliminary tests with cancerous mice showed remarkable results. But unfortunately humans did not respond in the same way. Eighteen patients were kept alive for five years but all had serious side reactions—too serious for the treatment to be continued.

An initial failure does not rule out further work. At Brookhaven the big reactor is being used in a technique developed by Dr. Sweet of Massachusetts General Hospital, to arrest tumors of the brain. These malignancies have a selective affinity for boron. If the patient is given a dose of the metal in soluble form it quickly seeks out the tumor. He is then placed beside the pile and a stream of neutrons is carefully directed through his head. The boron is made radioactive, emitting alpha particles of high energy, and these presumably destroy the cancer tissue.

The method may avoid the bad results obtained at Berkeley. Alphas, as we have seen, have extremely short range in tissue, and since they originate in the boron lodged in the target material, destroy only that.

Radiotherapy, so far, is directing its main guns upon cancers that are deep and unreachable by established methods. Radiation from outside by neutrons, by cobalt-60 gammas, by X-rays; radiation from within from selective chemicals; intensive research into the fundamental biology of cells and life processes—these are three points of attack upon humanity's most baffling disease.

Can we say that cancer will be conquered? Yes, though we cannot say when. Any day a basic discovery may suddenly unlock the secret.

Already there are "soft spots" in the enemy's flank. Work in M.I.T.'s high-voltage clinic, says the American Cancer Society, is controlling many deep tumors by electron beams. Radiogold solutions, administered as routine in many hospitals, are slowing down cancers of lung and abdomen. Radiohafnium has proved to be a powerful modifier of the action of the adrenal gland, while radiogallium may soon be accepted as a specific for cancer of the bone. Radiogold, furthermore, is giving highly encouraging results in the more intractable cases of prostate cancer and is protecting the unborn babies of cancerous mothers.

We can only make a sampling of the vast drive against this killer. It should be an encouraging sample, for hardly a day passes but some new achievement is published. The attack on cancer is something like an army looking for a lost lump of gold in a square mile of wilderness. Somebody is sure to find it; others, who do not, help narrow the search.

The hundreds of researches in progress will chip off small corners of the problem, many of them reducing the cancer hazard just a little. There will probably never be a sudden, front-page cure for the disease; rather, a gradual lessening of the threat till it is finally forgotten. This, at least, seems a proper prediction for this century. In the next, if we have not allowed the atom to annihilate us by then, we may have learned to rebuild bodies at will, as we now do houses.

(Last minute note): Sudden reversal of all prophecy is what makes science so exciting. Front pages of New York papers have just printed an announcement by the Sloane-Kettering Institute (mid-summer, 1954). They report that they have just developed a compound, TEM, which has proved to be 100 per cent effective in curing one type of cancer in rats! Results, says the official statement, "justify the hope that further study may reveal compounds capable of achieving permanent cure in man, not only of leukemia but eventually of other forms of cancer now beyond control."

Cautious, it is true. But they did use the word "cure" after all.

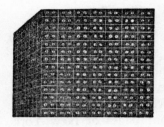

6. How Isotopes Are Made

· · · · · · · · · ·

‡   PRODUCTION AND shipment of radioisotopes today is a flourishing government business. The main "factories" so far are at Oak Ridge and Brookhaven, with minor aid from Argonne and Arco, Idaho. In Canada, Chalk River carries the whole burden for that nation, and for parts of Europe. Canada's piles carry on vigorous isotope research, as for instance, finding out the nutrition cycle of lake fish, learning why wharf piles corrode, controlling paper making to cut down rejects from variations in thickness.

Practically any element can be made radioactive in a pile, simply by sealing it in a small aluminum container and pushing it into a duct within the neutron atmosphere. A highly organized system of remotely controlled handling permits the material to be treated at a known intensity and for a known time. In some piles pneumatic tubes blow the containers in and out. At Chalk River samples are packed in metal balls and rolled into the pile by gravity. All handling is done in such a way that operators can work steadily without receiving radiation.

At Oak Ridge the procedure is on a mass-production basis, and all material is treated on a once-a-week schedule. The pile must be shut down to load and unload, so its work is scheduled in weekly cycles. This results in standardized radioactivity, each element coming out with its usual strength.

When a run shuts down the containers of new isotopes are withdrawn with long rods into heavy lead "pigs," and are stored. Another department is constantly busy, packing and shipping. When a laboratory orders, say, a curie of radio-strontium the material is taken out of storage, diluted to the right strength, and packed in lead for shipment. The type of activity determines how much shielding is necessary, according to Interstate Commerce Commission rules. If the isotope is an alpha or beta emitter only, little shielding beyond the shipping carton is needed. If it is a gamma emitter, lead is necessary, sometimes tons of it, where hundreds or thousands of curies are involved.

The actual amount of active material may be as little as $\frac{1}{100}$ or $\frac{1}{1000}$ of a gram. Ten thousand shipments from Oak Ridge to 1700 customers has been the yearly average, but the total of isotopic material may not be more than a single gram in a year.

In its big brick-and-steel factory called X-10 Oak Ridge produces mostly long-lived isotopes, which are flown to their destinations by commercial airlines, sometimes carried by express. Along with nearly half of the nation's output of U-235 for bombs, Oak Ridge also manufactures a small amount of non-radioactive isotopes in the old electromagnetic separation plant, Y-12. These are used in basic research where radioactivity would interfere with delicate measurements. As tracers, they can be detected by analysis in a mass spectrograph.

The Brookhaven setup is somewhat different. The big pile is not an isotope factory but a research facility, with isotope-making incidental. The pile has internal ducts so arranged that material to be converted goes through along a continuous loop. The cans of material are numbered and pushed in, one after another. Careful "maps" are kept so that the location of any can is always known. By moving the whole line around any sample can be removed at will. Thus, high or low activity can be given to it, and delivery can be made as soon as it is ready. The pile need not be shut down to load and unload.

Brookhaven makes only a few hundred shipments a year, mostly to the Atlantic seaboard area, to hospitals and university laboratories. These are either delivered by car or plane. On a typical morning a shipment, say, of radiosodium, in a compact little lead pot—it is a gamma emitter—is called for by Connie Schmidt, who has the contract for handling Brookhaven isotopes. Schmidt takes it to La Guardia Airport, 60 miles away, and sees it onto a plane, maybe for Boston. It is met at the other end by a truck from some hospital and is in the laboratory at work before noon.

While this is the history of the common isotopes like sodium, potassium and phosphorus, there are many demands for more specialized products, usually not in the chemical form produced in the pile. In such cases the raw material will be sent on to special manufacturing companies such as Abbott Laboratories or Tracerlab. Here, the radioisotopes are reacted with standard chemicals to make hundreds of highly complicated compounds that are needed in biochemical research.

Typical is carbon-14, which can be stored for centuries without appreciable weakening. The carbon can be built into complex organic molecules: alcohols, ethers, acids, amino acids and so on. Often it can be given a special location in the molecular structure—very important in hydrocarbon studies.

Leafing through Tracerlab's fat isotope catalogue, for instance, we find this among hundreds:

Citric Acid-1, 5-C^{14} . . .
$$HOOC^{14}CH_2C (OH) (COOH) CH_2C^{14}OOH$$

Note the staggering complexity of the formula (simple enough to the chemist); note, too, that the radiocarbon, C-14, occupies certain definite places in it. It is an extremely technical job to maneuver the radiocarbon into these places in the molecular structure, but it must be done as a routine job before frontier experiments in organic chemistry can be done and new knowledge gained.

Whatever the isotope or isotopic compound, it is delivered to the customer at a definite energy level. A tag fastened to the container tells what it is, mentions its half-life and gives the curie level of activity as of a certain date. Radioisotopes may be sold according to energy level, by the curie, as measured at the time of shipment. This is done at Oak Ridge. Or they may be sold as irradiated units, in which the activity is calculated from the length of exposure in the pile, as at Brookhaven. The so-called "processed units" from Oak Ridge are more accurately measured and more expensive. Brookhaven does not guarantee activity level within 20 per cent; its products are cheaper and calibration work must be done on them by the user.

But it is the fate of the radioisotope to be continually checked for activity. All through its life it is subjected to counter tests. In the pharmacist's laboratory you see half a dozen measuring jobs proceeding at once, each walled in by a castle of thick lead bricks. After use, wherever the isotope goes, into another experiment or down the drain, it is watched and accounted for till it finally dies.

One might think that the shipping of dangerous isotopes by common carrier would be a difficult thing, but it has not turned out to be. At first, package handlers were alarmed when they read the labels and thought of the bomb. Nowadays nobody pays much attention to isotopes; regulations are so strict that there is no more radiation outside the container than from natural sources in the surroundings. About 100,000 particles from cosmic rays and earth sources pass through your body every hour. Strays that penetrate shipping containers are much fewer than this.

The majority of radioisotope shipments go on a preferred basis, by air express. In England a great deal of expense is saved by carrying the stuff in a little well in the wing tip of the plane, with no shielding at all. The shipments are handled by trained men who use long rods to keep away from the field of danger. Wing tips are far enough away from passengers and crew to prevent radiation hazard.

At present, with AEC in complete control of the radio-isotope business, very rigid regulations for handling and use are maintained. No doctor or laboratory group may buy them unless they can show that they have sufficient training and experience. The price of isotopes is very low—hardly more than the cost of manufacture and handling, with nothing added for the gigantic investment in equipment. Soon after entering the business in 1946, AEC decided to give the product free to cancer research; more recently they have charged 20 per cent of the cost. This has meant in effect that the American people have staked science in the great fight.

The business is sure to grow into a large and permanent part of raw-material supply for research. AEC piles will be extended to cover the whole country, so that fast deliveries can be made anywhere. Today, AEC does a large foreign business but this is likely to taper off as other nations set up their own production lines. For many of the critically short-lived products cannot be sent abroad at all. Sodium-24, for example, an isotope in great demand in hospitals, loses ¾ of its potency in 30 hours. As many as 40 others have value in research and industry but weaken too fast to be shipped at all.

Interest is growing in the small, privately owned reactor

that can make isotopes in small amounts, doing research at the same time. Already the University of North Carolina has such a pile; Penn State has one on order; M.I.T. has announced plans for one. AEC welcomes these small, privately owned machines, paid for by the owners, who get subsidies from the government for carrying on research. They pay off to the nation in many ways, among them by teaching nuclear engineering and physics, thereby increasing the number of atomic experts for tomorrow.

Radioisotopes can't be made in power reactors because of the tight neutron economy necessary for efficiency. They can make fission products—they can't help it. And these may some day become invaluable to industry, as we shall see.

7. Atoms on the Farm

• • • • • • • •

THOUGH AGRICULTURE is probably man's oldest profession a good deal of it is still done by rule of thumb. Too little is known of the biochemical processes of plant growth. Yet scientific food raising is vital to feeding the world, with its swelling population and the rapid depletion of its soils. For this reason agriculture has been a focal point of radioisotope research ever since the war. The tracer technique is the world's first real method for making a close study of growth.

No problem is more important than the cracking of the great mystery of photosynthesis. How does a plant take in water and carbon dioxide through its leaves, energize them with sunlight, and produce the starches and sugars that build the marvelous complex of cellulose cells?

The problem had occupied science for a century when, in 1933, workers at Berkeley produced radioactive carbon-11 in the cyclotron. They found that this short-lived material could be built into carbon dioxide and traced through its history in photosynthesis—that is, part way. Principally, they discovered that the photochemical reaction is not simple but exceedingly complicated. Carbon-11, with a half-life of 20½ minutes, was too fleeting to tell them more.

199

When Oak Ridge began turning out carbon-14, with its half-life of 5580 years, the first effective tracer technique was possible for organic chemistry. Since then, great progress has been made; in a few years more photosynthesis should yield its secrets. It is already known that as many as 50 compounds are made by sunlight, water and CO_2, in the thin "plastids" of chlorophyll. In some of these the radiant energy is fixed or stored, somewhat as electrical energy is fixed in a storage battery. The compounds react with one another and eventually produce the sugars and starches. When food is eaten, the process is reversed and the end of it is muscular energy and carbon dioxide again.

It is supposed now that there are ten steps the plant goes through to make its substance. Six are fairly well understood; one, at least, does not require light at all. But even with the finest of modern tracer techniques it is supremely difficult to understand how the atoms join and rejoin, often at lightning speed. Utmost ingenuity and inspiration is needed to invent ways of tricking a little green leaf into showing its hand.

Dr. Melvin Calvin, a pioneer at Berkeley, says that sulfur plays an essential part along the way, accepting the light quanta from the chlorophyll molecules when they first strike and capturing them for permanent storage. Another pioneer, Dr. Sterling B. Hendricks, of the Department of Agriculture, points out that photosynthesis is of interest to mankind for two reasons; first, because it has led to all of our fossil fuels, hence is a basic concept in the production and use of energy. Second, that it has done as much as any one research to develop the techniques of radioactive tracers.

There are two main types of ambition in the minds of workers in this field, says Dr. Hendricks. Some hope that a knowledge of the growth process will eventually make it possible for us to do away with plants altogether, as food and fuel sources, making both in chemical factories. Others, less ambitious, hope to increase the efficiency of the solar reactions, now very poor, and thus increase food and fuel production. Plants, he points out, go to sleep in the middle of the day, unable to keep pace with the sun's lavish energy. If we can understand why the process has this flaw we may be able to correct it, and make an acre of land raise much more food.

A way-point in this complicated search for truth is the discovery that the green algae of the sea can be forced to produce very high food values—as much as 85 per cent fats. Even today, some think, a large-scale chemical industry could be based on these tiny plants, turning out an unlimited supply of palatable foods and combustible fuels.

It may be 10 or 20 years before the results are all in; meantime, radio-botany and -biology are very busy with simpler problems. Carbon-14 is a marvelous tool wherever life is concerned. According to Canadian scientists, if one teaspoonful of the isotope were distributed evenly through all the water of Lake Ontario, an accurate measure of the amount in one thimbleful of the mixture could be made.

An early practical use of radioisotopes in agriculture was to determine the function of fertilizers. Do they really help? In what stage of plant growth are they needed? Does each plant thrive best on a different food, or one differently applied? A few answers are in; it will be a fairly simple matter to get the rest, though it may take some time.

A typical early finding showed that the tobacco plant of the middle Atlantic seaboard cannot benefit from superphosphate fertilizer during its period of growth. North Carolina State College quickly broadcast this news and farmers in that state have been saving thousands of tons of phosphate formerly wasted.

Other research with tracers on fertilizers has shown the

way to better use and is now revealing the part played by minute traces of copper, molybdenum, zinc and iron in the soil. American farmers spend close to a billion dollars a year on fertilizers. They can well afford to improve their use in any way possible. Tracers offer the only known way of distinguishing between the effects of applied plant nutrients and those naturally occurring in the soil.

Growing things are extremely sensitive to minute amounts of chemicals in the soil and especially to various disease organisms. Tracer chemistry helps to identify these good and bad factors, often tying them together. Blights of various kinds are being traced to lack of certain nutrient factors, in the same way that anemia in humans is accounted for by lack of iron. Dutch elm disease is one that may be eradicated before long.

A lot of work is being done on the action of weed and insect killers. An estimated six billion dollars' worth of damage is done to trees and crops every year by fungi and insects. Successful use of poisons depends on knowing exactly how they function in the very small concentrations which are safe to use. Radioisotope tagging is virtually the only way that the action of these chemicals can be understood.

The pursuit of insects by radio-tracer is a minor miracle of science. In Oregon, flies have been fed on radiophosphorus and then released. When all possible flies have been trapped and tested for miles around, it is discovered that "hot" insects have traveled as far as 28 miles. The unsuspecting yellow fever mosquito has been tricked in the same way, in Africa, into revealing its migrating habits. The tests yield information that helps control the pests around settlements and encampments.

If you want to know what makes eggs grow inside of hens you can radioactivate their mash. An Oak Ridge scientist has done this and finds material in the eggs which the hens ate more than a month before. The shells, he says, are worked up at the last minute, within a day of laying.

A neat trick has been invented by R. C. Busland of the Department of Agriculture. He sterilizes large numbers of male screwworm flies by exposing them to cobalt-60, then frees them to mate in cattle-farming areas. Little by little the females lay unfertilized eggs and the species dies out in that area. At least, this is the indication. If the scheme works, cattlemen will be rid of one deterrent in fattening their herds.

Various types of aphid and mite have been controlled in California orange groves by tracer research on poisons. Mosquitoes have been tracked to their breeding grounds and wiped out by tagging them; the causes of blights of the peanut plant, soy beans, flax, clover and alfalfa have been identified and the diseases held back.

Parallel to these studies of practical farming improvement go researches into the fascinating field of genetics. It has long been known that good qualities as well as bad can be enhanced through the cultivation of mutations in normal plants. But until radiation techniques arrived, plant biologists had to wait for random mutations.

Thus, Brookhaven reports a new rust-resistant strain of oats, created by bombarding oat seeds with neutrons, then painstakingly selecting and propagating the mutation which had the resistant quality. Oats are our second largest cereal crop; a hardier plant will mean that nature can be made to remove some of the taxpayer's burden of subsidy to oat farmers.

Nearly a century ago Gregor Mendel discovered the tiny world of genetics—of the chromosomes and genes which subdivide with amazing fidelity to carry on the race. It is the duty of the thousands of genes, he discovered, to transmit characteristics from one generation to the next. Normally the genes reproduce themselves faithfully, but once in a million times or so there is a mistake and a mutation results. Generally, the result is bad; the new individual is inferior in some way. Only rarely does a mutation improve a characteristic.

When cells are broken apart by radiation they frequently rejoin in new ways, bringing about mutations hundreds of times as often as nature does. With this speeded-up process it is possible to "manufacture" good mutations almost on a production basis. Geneticists are now trying to build cell molecules containing radiocarbon, -phosphorus and -sulfur, so as to provide the internal cell radiation that will make these mutation factories work. At Brookhaven there is a large experimental field with a strong radiocobalt source at the center. Plants are set out in circular rows around it, and the effect of the radiation is measured in the mutations that turn up in the seed crop. Too much of it kills; too little does not affect the genes.

The achievement of rust-resistant oats is important because it was done in about two years, while the well-known discovery of hybrid corn by older methods took at least 20 years. The new corn has saved farmers tens of millions in lost crops. So it is obvious that radio-genetics offers a tremendous advantage to agricultural economy. But the path is still a long one, for only a few are skillful and patient enough to work in such a delicate field.

Even longer is the path of improvement for animals and, eventually, for man himself. At present, a good deal of work is being done on flies, mice and fish. For instance, female salmon that were about to spawn were X-rayed at the University of Washington. When the eggs were laid they were artificially fertilized in the laboratory. Six months later the resulting fingerlings were marked and put into the ocean. On their return the following year, marked fish were paired. The process was repeated through four generations.

The principal conclusion so far is that abnormalities were

far above normal, but the researchers hope that good characteristics will turn up that can be built upon to increase the salmon's value. A similar run has been made on trout. Possibly, some day, the eager angler can go out, confident that he *can't* catch anything less than a 30-pound whopper!

Geneticists could not be working with radioactivity without wondering about the effects of radiation from the bombs. Dr. A. H. Sturtevant, of California Institute of Technology, recently sounded a very sober warning. Although he admits that the world-wide radiation from the test-bomb explosions is extremely low, and harmless to people now living, it is by no means harmless to unborn generations. The steady, low-intensity irradiation of the whole world population, he says, is bound to result in cumulative genetic effects that will be permanent. "There is no recovery of damaged genes."

"There is no possible escape from the conclusion," Dr. Sturtevant insists, "that the bombs already exploded will ultimately result (in future generations) in the production of numerous defective individuals—if the human species survives for many generations. And every new bomb exploded, since its radioactive products are widely dispersed over the earth, will result in an increase in this ultimate harvest of defective individuals."

It is unpopular to worry about our great-great-great-grandchildren. But if ever there was a time when we should do so, it is now.

8. Industry Meets the Atom

RADIATION MAY influence civilization most profoundly through such unsuspected means as these, but its greatest present appeal is likely to be in industry. Here it offers a greater challenge to America's inventive genius than any discovery in history. Its applications are as numerous as the uses of the wheel or the threaded screw.

Even now, at the beginning, it is impossible to enumerate all of the ways in which radioisotopes can help industry. We can only make a sampling of the field. Here are a few highlights:

The Bell Telephone Laboratories, a few years ago, began using radiostrontium in studies to improve the preservation of telephone poles. Tens of thousands of these poles rot away every year because the tars used to impregnate them don't penetrate properly. Samples of pole wood were soaked in the isotope solution, then sliced thin. Laid on photographic film, they produced "radioautographs," showing just where the liquid had concentrated in the fine capillaries. Better drying methods and better preservative chemicals now make the poles last much longer. A small discovery, but one that can be reflected in your telephone bill.

A homely example of a better product is this: a floor wax maker had the U.S. Testing Company construct a big roller, with several shoe soles glued to it. As new waxes are formulated, the roller is walked back and forth over surfaces coated with them. The waxes all have radio-tags in them. A counter survey of the sample and soles quickly tells which wax will stay down longest and remain brightest.

Wear is a field of study in which isotopes are ideal detectors. Shoe soles themselves can be tested, so can automobile tires, paint, concrete, metals, even the hardest steel. Standard Oil of California developed the widely advertised RPM engine

oil with the help of isotope research at M.I.T. In the tests, engine piston rings were sent to Oak Ridge for radiation treatment in the pile. Installed in laboratory engines and run with a variety of lubricants, they soon told which oil best prevented friction. A poorly oiled cylinder permits piston-ring wear; a good one produces less steel dust to be ground off the ring.

An unexpected finding in this project is that engines wear out faster in traffic than they do when driven cross-country at 70 miles an hour. Standard claims that the same information about oil, obtained by old-time chemical methods, would have cost a million dollars and required 60 years. The whole research, with radioisotopes, is expected to cost $35,000, and take four.

Isotope work at the Chrysler Corporation is directed at the basic causes of wear between rubbing surfaces. Whether you run an engine fast or slow, or idle it, doesn't seem to be important. Worst wear is at the ends of the piston stroke. It is now believed that "wear" is in fact the welding of tiny elements of the metal surfaces, then the tearing loose of the welds. It is like running a plow over a field. Friction, of course, is the principal power thief of the world. The Chrysler studies should lead to still better oils and the coating of surfaces with metals that do not weld.

Arthur D. Little, Inc., industrial chemists, recently made a tracer study for Oneida Silver, to find out why ammonia added to a silver plating bath improves the surface. With radiosulfur in the ammonia they found that the NH_3 breaks up the silver crystals as they are deposited, producing a finer grain. An "extra dividend" in this research showed, surprisingly, that the century-old theory of electroplating had been slightly wrong. When it is corrected the processes should give us better looking and more durable plating.

Uses for radioisotopes in industry are increasing so fast that manufacturers of radiation equipment publish long lists of applications. One list mentions 70 different *classes* of use which every industrialist who is up to date should know about.

For example there is process control: measuring and monitoring all sorts of things such as the thickness of steel sheets and plastic films, the level of liquids in tanks, the uniformity of paint and enamel coatings. Then there is testing: the tarnish resistance of silver plate, the effectiveness of soaps, the answers to posers such as how long a film of toothpaste protects your teeth, how deep does cold cream penetrate your skin, how thoroughly do dry cleaning methods remove spots? And there are the applications in the service industries: where are buried pipes leaking? How do you find a manhole lost in the snow? How long will an asphalt highway last?

Any ingenious person can come up with new ways to use isotopes if he lets his imagination roam. Such as protecting a dangerous machine with radiation-operated alarms and controls. If the operator's hand comes too close, a small isotope source he is wearing rings a bell and stops the machine.

The point is, suddenly we have means of finding out how things are going among the armies of molecules where individual soldiers could never be seen or controlled before. Able now to make our orders heard among these individuals, we can send the armies out on entirely new campaigns.

One of the most vigorous pleas to jump on the radioisotope bandwagon is an article printed in April, 1953, by McGraw-Hill's *Factory Management and Maintenance Magazine*, from which I am permitted to quote in part:

HOW YOU, TOO, CAN USE RADIOISOTOPES

You might say, "There's nothing in it for me." But there can be—if you have problems in inspection, quality control, chemical process control; if you make anything in continuous sheet, if you want to keep your maintenance department up to date.

"That's strictly lab stuff now." But it's not, by a long shot. Take a look at FACTORY's survey. You'll see that not only are companies using radioisotopes to solve plant problems today, but they're doing it right in the plant, not in the laboratory.

"Too dangerous. I'm afraid to start with it." But you shouldn't be. Radioisotopes are no more dangerous than any of the other potential hazards you now have under control.

A high-voltage line is dangerous, too. So are toxic chemicals. But you manage to protect against them. And protecting against radioisotopes won't be especially involved for you.

"Don't want to hire an atomic physicist to tell me what to do." But who said you had to? FACTORY's survey points out that most plants don't have specialists in radioactivity. They hire an outside consultant. And they rely on operating people with little more information on the subject than they get, in many cases, from AEC literature.

"Costs too much to get in the act." But it doesn't. Costs some to get started. So does any piece of equipment you need for a new technique. But isotopes pay off, and pay off fast in material saved, in better product quality, in less rejects, in less labor, in lower-cost maintenance.

"I won't know what to do when something goes hay-wire." But you will. In most cases you'll be able to correct the trouble just as you would on any other electronic or electrical equipment. The radioisotope is a foolproof source. Only spot trouble can develop is in the rest of the equipment.

"Too much government red tape." But there's actually very little. You use the isotopes only if AEC is satisfied you can handle them safely and effectively. To prove to AEC that you can, you have to submit a written form answering a series of questions. And there's no further red tape.

"I'll lose customers if they think my product may be radioactive." But you can relax on that score. No chance for your product to have any radioactivity if it is merely exposed to radiation. Where you use the radioisotope in processing—where they become part of your product—you choose such a radioisotope and use it in such a way that there's no more radioactivity in your product by the time it's sold than there is in an ordinary glass of milk.

"Don't want to get mixed up in one of those hush-hush security deals." Companies that use radioisotopes have no security problem. No screening of employees, no silence about plant processes.

This lively argument covers pretty much all of the objections which an uninformed manufacturer might raise against the new atomic tool. It is certainly a challenge to anyone who wants to modernize.

Basic questions for any businessman are whether radioisotopes will save him money and whether his workers will accept the idea and co-operate to make it work. To answer these questions Factory sent out questionnaires to 80 companies using istotopes. Better than half of them said that the isotope devices, which they used in hundreds of different ways, would pay for themselves in savings *within two years.* This is five times faster than conventional rates of amortization on experimental devices. The rest of the companies agreed that it would take a little longer to reach the break-even point, but not much.

In general, it costs from $2,000 to $10,000 for the average plant to set up with radiation monitoring.

As to how radioisotope equipment was accepted by the plant force, the overwhelming majority believed that workers took to it without dismay, as a natural part of the atomic age. The few cases where timidity cropped up were corrected by education and demonstrations of safety.

9. Isotopes Help Your Business

· · · · · · · · · · · ·

RADIOISOTOPES IN industry fall into two well-defined categories: the use of relatively weak products manufactured by special piles; the use of powerful fission products and high-energy sources such as cobalt-60. The first includes standardized isotopes for tracing, measuring and indicating. The second comprises radiation substitutes for X-ray machines, controls for massive machinery, etc.

Continuing with the first group: an ingenious and dramatic application of the incredibly small bursting atom is in thickness gauges. Thousands of products must be made to very close "tolerances" to be acceptable, even in the home. A shoestring that is weak, cigarette paper with holes in it, chromium plating that wears off too fast; these and innumerable other shortcomings must be avoided. At the express-train speed of mass production hairline controls of quality must work automatically and without fail.

Pliofilm, used in all sorts of ways around the house and in merchandising, is a fine example. It is rolled out in great machines traveling continuously at high speed. Only a few thousandths of an inch thick, it must not vary from standard by as much as a ten-thousandth. Radioisotope gauges do the job today. The old way was to stop the machines every little while and make hand measurements with elaborate gauges, wasting time and bringing in the chance of human error.

The isotope thickness gauge is simple enough. Beneath the fast-running film is a small source of radiostrontium, which throws out beta particles at a perfectly steady rate—its half-life is 20 years. Just above this, on top of the film, a Geiger tube is supported on an arm. Wires lead to an electronic amplifier and counter. Since the plastic film cuts down the radiation that passes through it, any variation in the count will indicate a change in its thickness. An indicating meter is calibrated to read in fractions of a ten-thousandth.

The device goes further. If a flaw or uneven place comes along electronic switches turn the machine off instantly, so that the faulty piece can be cut out.

Automatic thickness gauges are used in making linoleum, paper, rubber, tin plate and steel sheet. Steel is perhaps the most important. In the great mills the sheet is rolled out hot at breakneck speed—40 miles an hour or more. Flaws would be gone without recall before any of the older methods could announce them. Radioisotope robots, however, work almost at the speed of light, and can bring the whole mill to a stop in a few feet if trouble turns up.

One more sample will show the great diversity of the atomic monitor: its use in the oil industry. Here, the gamble of finding new oil pools is still as great as betting on the horses. Some 87 per cent of the wells drilled today are "dry holes." But they cost an average of $100,000 apiece, dry or not. Highly sensitive atomic exploration is already saving millions in useless drilling.

There is always some gamma radiation shooting upward from the ground. Over an oil pool usually there is a little less, but around the edges a little more than normal. This is called a "halo." The radiation is brought to the surface by oil and gas seeping through. It can be detected as high as 500 feet in the air. By mapping the halo with great care, the size and shape of the oil pool may be predicted.

First, a careful geophysical search is made for the right kind of oil formation. Seismographic tests further help to identify the deep strata. If the results are promising enough to justify it, radiometric tests are run. Special counters are flown over the area, back and forth on an accurate grid. The plotted records yield a radiation contour map that will reveal the halo if there is one.

Geiger counters are not sensitive enough for this work, so scintillation instruments are used—100 times as responsive to gammas. They are mounted in "coaxial" helicopters, whose double rotors hold them very steady, and are flown slowly over the area. After the aerial map is plotted, ground crews go over promising terrain with good Geiger counters and locate the probable centers of the oil domes below. A field may be entirely delineated in a few days; the old method of drilling "by feel" might take years.

Radiometry was first used in Canada, where the scintillation counter was invented, at the University of Manitoba. T. Lundberg, a Canadian mining engineer, claims to have opened several new oil fields by radiation methods. A number of promising new areas in Texas and Oklahoma, Illinois and Indiana, owe their discovery to it. And of course uranium exploration today depends on it.

Scintillation counter techniques will probably be the preferred means of discovering future oil, increasing reserves and saving vast sums now wasted because it is so difficult geologically to predict where oil will be found.

One intriguing reminder: "Anybody" can buy himself a scintillation counter and go hunting for oil, or uranium. All it takes is about $1,000, an airplane and the endurance of an ox. Naturally, too, a little luck.

The oil industry also uses radiation to simplify the problem of pumping different kinds of products through long pipe lines. The practice is to "ship" gasoline, then crude oil, then lubricants, and to know just when one "slug" ends and the next begins, for they must be switched to different tanks at the receiving end. Just as one slug ends at the sending station, a machine automatically injects a little radioactive material, which blends with the liquid. A counting device at the destination point picks up the "interface" unerringly and gives a warning. Switching can be done without stopping the flow.

Hundreds of industries today are convinced that radioisotopes can help them toward better products and less expense. But there should be thousands. The businessman's reluctance probably centers around his fear of the bomb and his unwillingness to trust anyone in his plant with responsibility for the new gadgets.

The simple answer to his doubts is special training for the people who are involved. A first step is to send a plant engineer or laboratory man to an atomic energy school to get the basic facts. The best of these is maintained by AEC at Oak Ridge, and courses as short as four weeks are given, for a $25 fee. Several of the colleges have opened similar courses; a few large industries such as Westinghouse also take in special students. In the near future we shall probably see courses in radioisotope theory and handling offered by the technical night schools and even in adult training programs. AEC is doing everything it can to promote the idea.

As soon as a responsible company employee has been trained, any one of many suppliers of radiation equipment can be consulted. Numerous specialists are available for consultation; they can soon advise plant executives how to use the new tool to best advantage. You will be able to call in a consulting firm in any large city; they will be as common some day as law firms. These people will help you get set up and will instruct your people in the use of the equipment. Your only other beginner's problem is to make sure that personnel is properly trained for the job.

Factory Management puts it snappily: *

Do You Need an Employee Training Program?

If you do, you'll probably want to use one or more of the following methods now in common practice.

*Sponsor Lectures. You may be able to get AEC people to come to your plant for talks. Also, you can have various staff people, your consultant, or your isotope supplier make an informal talk before the people directly concerned with radioisotopes.

*Show Films. There are several good films on radioisotopes available from both the AEC and private organizations.

*Encourage reading of books and pamphlets. It will pay you to try to acquaint your employees with further information on the job. Keeping a "help-yourself" bookshelf of material on radiation will both give your employees confidence and help them learn their jobs better.

There is really no difference between the new radiation gadgets and hundreds of electronic, chemical and mechanical specialties that crop up in a plant all the time. No one is timid about them. If they are dangerous, manufacturer's cautions are followed. Many of the isotope devices are now standard items. The plant need have no more knowledge of their internal workings than of a good public address system. Radiation is just another form of energy, harnessed to do useful work.

A word belongs here about patents. If your technical

* Same article as referred to before.

people develop a useful device around radioisotopes, can you protect it? AEC has been fairly liberal in interpreting the patent restrictions of the Atomic Energy Act, which deal mainly with devices concerned with fissionable material, weapons, etc. The commission now rules that "inventions or discoveries made by persons using radioisotopes or using or manufacturing isotope-labeled compounds will be subject to patenting by the inventor in accordance with normal industrial practices."

This opens a vast new field—one that might become as fruitful and as profitable as the fabulous electronics industry.

Suppose you have decided to take a flyer in radioistopes in your plant. How do you get official sanction? First, you get in touch with AEC's Field Advisory Service, a section of the Isotopes Division at Oak Ridge, Tennessee. They will send you booklets and information as to consultants, suppliers of materials and instruments, and so on. They will probably refer you, also, to a consultant in your region. He will take it from there.

If you prefer to go slower, discussing and gathering information without hiring anybody, AEC will gladly be your guide. The commission does not run a consulting service but in the early stages it is anxious to give you all the information available to the public.

When the time comes to buy your first isotopes you will, of course, have a staff set up to handle the details. There is some AEC paper work to do at this stage—certain forms to be filled out for your supplier. Not much information is required; it is not an income tax nightmare. You simply have to satisfy AEC that you have put a competent person in charge of your isotope work, that you have complied with safety regulations and have the necessary equipment for checking your workers for radiation exposure.

AEC makes no inspection of your setup, though it may drop in any time to see how things are going. Once you've got your authorization to buy isotopes you're an active and responsible member of the atomic age.

It is a mistake to think that only very large plants can get into the isotope game. No business is too small to receive advice and guidance from the atomic authorities. In fact, the Small Business Administration distributes a special bulletin (No. 31): "Radioisotopes and Small Business," which gives good basic information and illustrated examples of isotope use in small plants.

The uninitiated might think that a good beginning for radioisotopes would be to make golf ball cores of them. Then you could go around the links after the game with a Geiger counter and find all the balls you lost. Unfortunately, it doesn't work. The chief engineer of a consulting firm tried it and gave it up. Radiation had to be so strong that he would have had to play his game by remote control.

The present author invented the same thing, as hundreds more probably have, with similar results. The best thing to do with isotopes at the golf club is to talk about them.

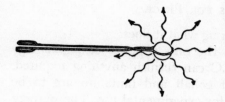

10. High-Energy Radiation

• • • • • • • • •

WHAT MIGHT be called the "senior division" in industrial isotope work involves the use of high-powered radiations. It is an extremely dangerous field because the rays can produce fatal injury in accidental exposures of only a few seconds. However, such radiation is so valuable in industry that it will probably take the lead in a few years.

High-energy radiation can be obtained in three ways: from metals like cobalt and strontium, "soaked" in an atomic pile for long periods, from atomic fission products and by neutron bombardment from the pile itself. So far only laboratory samples of fission products have been tried out and they are not yet on the market. High-energy work today is practically all done with cobalt and strontium.

In this field the isotope is used as a source of massive amounts of energy for penetrating heavy metal or for promoting chemical reactions. The measurement unit is the curie rather than the milli-curie, as in medicine. A few sources run up as high as 10,000 curies. Most industrial radiation work can be done with a few curies. The cost of sources usually runs between $1 and $100 per unit. This may seem expensive for a large installation, but the cost is nominal compared to $15,000 to $20,000 per curie for radium. Cobalt, of course, loses half its potency in five years and is virtually worthless after 20 years.

Even so, it is cheap considering what it does.

Chalk River has been the only supplier of high-energy sources till lately; now AEC can furnish anything required. Thousand-curie isotopes of cobalt and tantalum are to be made available to industry for experimental use. The purpose is to explore the industrial value of high radiation to see if the government should begin releasing fission products. If there is enough demand, these would no doubt be much less expensive per curie.

The main industrial use for radiation sources today is in radiography—the photographing of metals to detect flaws. X-rays have been used for years for this work. Flaw-detection is considered essential for high-pressure vessels, piping and tanks, for castings which must stand great stress, for welded parts subjected to vibration, etc. Crank shafts for large diesels are routinely X-rayed; rivet fastenings on big tanks must be "looked into"; so must the bodies of high-pressure valves and the breech assemblies of guns.

X-ray photography, however, is expensive and the apparatus for it often weighs tons. The same results can be had from a powerful isotope of thimble size, contained in shielding about the dimensions of a barrel.

Comparing the two, C. A. Karrer of Milwaukee's Crucible Steel Casting Co. says that isotopes for radiography cost about $1,000, with negligible maintenance, while equivalent X-ray apparatus is worth $45,000 with much added expense for upkeep. This breakdown is of real interest to the small plant.

Very few businessmen yet realize the potentialities of industrial radiation. AEC, anxious to find a use for its rapidly accumulating fission products, is pioneering the field vigorously. One of its principal assistants in this is the Stanford Research Institute of Palo Alto, California. A year or two ago SRI received a cobalt source from Brookhaven, consisting of a

rod about the size of a baseball bat, composed of several concentric tubes. It was rated at 4500 curies and had required 237
days continuous neutron bombardment in the pile. It is said
to be equivalent to $80 million worth of radium. It crossed the
country in a lead container of ash-can size, which held stray
radiation down to less than that of a wrist watch. But in its
resting place in a 5400-gallon pool of water (and no other
shield) it fills the water with an eerie blue glow like a distant
fire.

The Stanford group is a private consulting firm not connected with the university, set up to do just such survey work
as AEC needed for its fission products. The study, currently in
progress, is partly based on experiments with the cobalt source.
Mainly, however, it is a survey of industrial needs in the radiation field. Stanford's conclusion is that a brilliant future lies
ahead for radiation techniques, some of which are these:

Sterilization.

Some years ago scientists at M.I.T. began work on a
method of food preservation far different from refrigeration.
Similar work by the U.S. Army's Quartermaster Corps and the
American Meat Institute Foundation ran concurrently. The
experiments were based on the idea that food, once sterilized
by radiation, would not spoil. It is well known that radiation
kills bacteria; in fact, ultra-violet light has been used for steri-
lizing room air and certain drugs for many years. Early research
was done with X-rays, but lately all the emphasis has been on
isotope radiation.

The question to be settled is: can radiosterilization be accomplished economically and without damage to the food?
There is no conclusive answer to this yet. Serious problems
must first be solved. If they are solved, the advantages will be
great. Heat sterilization, the present standard method, destroys

some vitamins and impairs flavor. Refrigeration does not kill putrefaction bacteria but only delays them. Some products, notably drugs like penicillin, are made useless by heating. Intricate vacuum and chemical processes are needed for them. Penicillin production is a $100-million-a-year business and it costs at least $5 million to insure adequate chemical sterilization. If radiation can be made safe, a simple exposure to gamma

or beta rays will do the same job cold, *after* the drug has been sealed into its package. No further contamination can reach it.

Early food-irradiation experiments have been encouraging. Apples, rayed for a few minutes, have kept for four months without losing their firmness or bloom. Sterilized cake and cookie mixes stay fresh months longer. Packaged meat, which has a shelf life of only three days in the usual market display refrigerator, has remained edible at room temperature for more than two weeks, after irradiation. Researchers believe that little of the flavor or food value will be lost.

According to Dr. Howard Gottlieb of the University of Wisconsin, the radio-sterilization of meat is a proved thing. The only remaining problem, he says, is to find a gamma-ray source competitive with refrigeration methods.

A fascinating part of the project is to determine what amount of radiation will kill the bacterial ability to reproduce, without actually killing the germs themselves. If this turns out to be small, light doses may be sufficient and the danger of hurting flavor may be eliminated.

While a market full of irradiated foods may be some distance in the future, we can expect to see *surface* sterilization very soon. Products like eggs, fresh vegetables and grapes can be "fixed" to last a long time. Radiation, incidentally, is said to make cheap Puerto Rican rum taste much better. Presumably it would not last a long time at all.

Argonne Laboratory recently delivered to M.I.T. a radiation source consisting of nothing but a barrel of concrete. The active material is the concrete itself, made with water solutions of fission products. The mass has a small hole in its center into which samples to be radiated can be lowered by remote control. If it works well, it will be a dirt-cheap way to do sterilization.

Dr. Chauncey Starr of North American Aviation proposes a still cheaper way—after investment costs are met. Small reactors, he suggests, can be installed by food makers and the products can be inserted in the piles themselves, or exposed to the cooling fluid outside. Such an outfit would have the enormous value of killing trichinosis in pork very inexpensively. Today only about 20 per cent of the pork on the market has been treated for this dangerous parasite; more than a quarter of our population has, or has had, the disease.

Ionization.

When radiation strikes a gas such as air, or the cells of living tissue, it knocks off electrons, leaving "ions" or charged particles behind. "Ion" is from the Greek, meaning "wanderer." These particles have the power to conduct electricity; in fact, they are electricity when they are in motion. There are many ways in which ionization can be used effectively in industry.

A very serious problem in the making of nonmetallic products is the high-voltage electric charge generated in them by friction or induction. In powder plants, paint works and oil refineries "static" can start disastrous fires. Printing plants are hounded by the sticking of charged paper sheets. Especially in yarn and plastics plants, static must be dealt with if production is to be kept up.

The old way was to discharge the potential with metal "cat's whiskers," or by keeping the atmosphere very damp. The new way is to interpose a radioisotope where the static is generated, continually discharging it by ionization of the surrounding air. The Canadian atomic energy project, for instance, manufactures the "ionotron" static eliminator, consisting of long bars plated with gold or platinum containing radioisotopes which give off alpha particles. This is widely used in the paper industry.

A more familiar use of ionization by radiation is in fluorescent lamps. The voltage at which these lamps work is much lower than the starting voltage, so that rather heavy equipment must be installed in the fixture to give the necessary starting kick. A very small amount of radioactive material, built into the lamp, will keep it permanently ionized so that it will start and run on the same low voltage. The lamp will light at once, as a filament lamp does.

Such lamps have been developed and made ready for marketing. But there is a snag. Warehousing large numbers of them might concentrate radiation and endanger the handlers. Stiff regulations will have to be made and enforced.

Theoretically, a fluorescent lamp can be made to burn by internal radiation, without any current at all. The principle is already at work on the luminous dial of your watch. Producing useful light is only a step upward in energy, and it can probably be done with beta-emitters. Trouble is, there is danger present for home use. Such "lifetime" lamps would have to be encased in heavy plastic to hold the radiation inside. This has already been done successfully in a kind of plastic "sandwich" that lights up. It opens the intriguing possibility of a home lighted by its own walls.

Farther into the future is the possibility of promoting combustion by radio-ionization. Gasoline engines work because the flame that starts at the spark plug spreads by heat ionization. If the fuel mixture were slightly radioactive the flame would travel much more evenly. Stanford Research Institute has this to say:

"Control of the burning rate in internal combustion engines by ionizing the air-fuel mixture might prevent knocking. Incorporating a long-half-life beta-emitting isotope, such as strontium-90, might allow the use of lower-octane fuel."

And here is a really promising prospect: if you put a little piece of beta-emitting strontium-90 on an insulated metal post in a vacuum tube it will gradually charge itself by losing electrons. You then have what amounts to a battery. Experiments have shown that some 365,000 volts can be generated in this way. If some scheme is found to cut down this voltage and substitute for it an appreciable current, one can imagine a small portable source of electric power that would last 20 years—a flashlight that would burn indefinitely, perhaps.

The "bugs"? Strontium-90 would have to cost next to

nothing to compete with the highly efficient dry cells you use now.

"Hot" Chemistry.

There is no professional group more excited about the use of radioisotopes than the chemists. A strange new world of reactions that are speeded up, changed or stopped altogether, appears when radiation is present.

The general idea is that when a molecule in a chemical solution is struck by a radioactive particle, it is mutilated. Sometimes the charged particle replaces an ordinary one; sometimes it goes on, leaving molecular fragments behind. Sometimes it excites the whole neighborhood into unusual activity. Almost nothing is yet known of these things. Much of the preliminary work has been done by Dr. Willard F. Libby, one of the world's great theoretical chemists, working at the University of Chicago.

The uses of radiation chemistry, says Dr. Libby, will no doubt be highly technical. They will, for the most part, produce results not possible before. To illustrate this, he speaks of a research recently conducted, in which gasoline fractions have been made radioactive for the purpose of studying knocking in engines. This is an achievement in organic chemistry formerly very difficult, and gives the petroleum chemist a new tool to work with. Already, the Humble Oil Company in Texas is experimenting with the idea that radiations may offer a new way to catalyze the cracking process and improve the quality of gasolines and oils.

The best promise of "hot" chemistry lies on the organic side, where carbon, oxygen and hydrogen combine to form hundreds of thousands of compounds. Carbon-14, indispensable as a tracer, is often very difficult to place exactly where it is desired in the molecular structure. "Hot-atom" chemistry offers a means of doing this fairly easily. The location of the atoms in specific positions must be under the chemist's control if he is to synthesize new compounds, or do the extremely delicate pioneer work in biochemistry.

Today's drive in chemistry is to find out how nature's host of molecules are built. Tomorrow's will be to build new ones to exact requirements: woods as hard and durable as iron, cloth that can't wear out, fuels that can be made out of air and energy in a few days. It is dangerous to predict, for science is always turning some corner that reveals a totally new world.

Radiation chemistry has already made one practical contribution of major importance. It has found that isotopes can do surprising things in plastics and synthetic rubber. Plastics are usually made in a two-stage process called polymerization. Organic molecules brought together in solution are welded by heat into long chains which give them flexibility and toughness. But the product isn't very strong and won't stand much heat.

The amazing growth in types and properties of plastics still hasn't solved these problems. It had not, that is, until scientists tried irradiating a finished plastic dish with million-volt electrons. The result was a harder, considerably more heat-resistant material. Dr. Guy Suits, head of General Electric's Research Laboratories, where the work was done, believes a new type of plastic is now possible—one that will stand the heat of boiling and thus give us a whole new line of containers.

Chemists explain the improvement as a process of cross-linking already long molecules into a stronger fabric. One can see a tremendous future for such "radio-cured" plastics—dishes that will survive the hottest wash water without curling or fraying; substitution of unbreakable bottles in which medicines can be sterilized after sealing; a whole class of cooking utensils, baby bottles, hospital ware. On the rubber side, tires that will stand light without deteriorating, garden hose that will last for years, waterproof garments and gloves that are more durable.

Chemistry is probably the largest single field in modern technology; the opportunities for radiation in it are tremendous. Perhaps in the next 20 years we shall be living in a new world.

II. The Radiation Calendar

• • • • • • • • • • •

DR. LIBBY is responsible for a isotopic tool that looks *back*, not ahead. This is the fascinating radiocarbon dating process, which can determine with remarkable accuracy the age of ancient relics as far back as two hundred centuries. It can be used on any fragment which contains carbon—carving, weaving, remains of wood structures, manuscripts, plants, animals, even human bones. The technique at present can date such remains with an error of only 10 per cent.

Dr. Libby does it by measuring the extremely tiny radiations of carbon-14 in the sample and comparing this value with the amount he calculates was in it when it was made. Knowing the half-life of the carbon isotope to be about 5600 years, simple arithmetic establishes the antiquity.

The brilliant discovery that makes this possible was that the proportion of radiocarbon in any living material, anywhere, at any time in history, is constant. One gram of carbon, Libby explains, built into a tree, say, will contain enough of the rare isotope to produce about 16 beta particles per minute. This level, which can be measured fairly closely with a scintillation counter, remains the same as long as the tree lives. When it dies, and no more new carbon is added by metabolism, the radiation gradually decreases to half in 5600 years, a quarter

229

in 11,200, an eighth in 16,800 and so on.

Libby's triumph was to devise a technique of measurement so delicate that he could distinguish between the count he wanted and the stray radiation in the air, many times as high. An accuracy of 10 per cent, while not very great in everyday affairs, is phenomenal, considering the obstacles involved.

Carbon-14 gets into all living things by the fixation of carbon dioxide always in the air. Dr. Libby has shown that the isotope is constantly being created there by cosmic ray bombardment, and that the amount of it present is substantially the same all the time. Now, all living things on the earth are built of carbon that originated in this CO_2 in the air. Plants on land and sea take it up initially; animals eat the plants, humans eat the animals and the plants, too. Thus, everything that lives has this same carbon radiation standard. Scientists believe that cosmic rays, perhaps caused by showers of atomic particles hurled at us from sun and stars, have been constant for millions of years.

Libby's dating process begins with an analysis of the sample to determine exactly what proportion of it is carbon. Next, he uses a counter, or group of counters and intricate shielding, that picks up every particle emanating from it, with the smallest possible error. And finally, by elaborate computation and test, he rules out the background count of particles produced by local radioactivity and cosmic rays.

A great deal depends on the identification of the radiation. It is like measuring the sound of a pin falling in a boiler shop going full blast. This means intimate knowledge of all radiation sources. The state of this knowledge is none too complete today, and this accounts in part for the relatively large error of 10 per cent.

Radiocarbon dating will probably be adopted by archaeologists as the standard method of determining the dates of ancient civilizations. More than 500 such dates have already been computed. Thus, Dr. Libby's group locates the last Ice Age at 11,000 years ago, and the oldest population at 10,000. Many of the dates have been cross-checked against results by older methods, and prove to be quite as accurate as Dr. Libby claims.

But he admits he has only started. An associate, Dr. James Arnold, has built a new type of "screen-wall" counter, believed to be some 10,000 times as sensitive as the conventional Geiger counter. It measures a sample after it has been dissolved in an organic liquid, held at a temperature of 20 degrees below zero. The researchers believe that with this they can eventually reduce their errors to a matter of 17 years instead of 1000.

Recently Dr. Libby has chalked up another triumph of isotopic dating that is even more exacting in its method. It uses the natural tritium (hydrogen-3) in the clouds and in ground water to determine the life history of the water for the past 20 years.

Tritium, whose man-made counterpart is an ingredient of the hydrogen bomb, is composed of one proton and two neutrons; it is mildly radioactive, with a half-life of about 12½ years. Libby believes it is made by bombardment of neutrons knocked loose from atoms in the upper air by cosmic rays, mostly at an altitude of some seven miles. These neutrons, hitting nitrogen atoms, produce carbon-14 and tritium. Eventually the tritium combines with oxygen to form triple-heavy water and falls with the rain. All the tritium in the world at any one time, Dr. Libby believes, amounts to no more than two pounds. Distributed throughout the atmosphere, some 30 atoms send off weak beta particles every minute. This results in a radioactive concentration so small that only the finest detection methods will give results. Nevertheless Dr. Libby has shown that it is possible to tell with reasonable accuracy how long a sample of tritium-containing water has been on the ground. He hopes that his method may be useful in tracing water back to its source and thus help in planning long-range water supplies.

Tritium dating could be used, Libby suggests, in determining the age of vegetable products such as flour and canned or frozen foods. It could be of more value in long-range weather prediction. Here it would give an indication of how various masses of moisture-laden air are mixed, hence tell where the air masses come from and how long they have been on the way.

Tritium counting requires the ultimate in fine measurement. The Chicago group can detect a single exploding tritium atom in ten billion billion atoms of ordinary hydrogen. The feat requires the concentration of some 30 gallons of the original sample by electrolysis, down to a few drops, but these few contain all the tritium in that sample. Then the arduous work of counting begins.

Dr. Libby has extended his study of tritium to many parts of the earth and he finds that the isotope fall varies widely, from very high at inland Chicago to very low on the seacoast, where rainwater comes from the sea. One of the amusing uses for the technique is in dating wines. Libby has studied domestic and French wines and has established the average tritium content for many vintages. Once a complete table has been made it will be possible to ignore the label on a bottle and find out how genuinely old your wine is by measuring its tritium content. This might delay drinking it a little.

"The fact that tritium can be measured in such extreme dilutions," says the Chicago scientist, "makes it an excellent tracer material—one which should have many industrial applications. Tritium is one of the cheapest isotopes to make (1000 times cheaper than carbon-14 from the atomic piles), and one of the safest to handle."

It is safe because its lone beta ray has very little energy. It might be cheap to use because so many industrial processes include water, which would be an ideal carrier for the tritium.

DANGER

RADIATION

12. Isotopes and Safety
• • • • • • • • •

ALL RADIOISOTOPES are potentially dangerous to humans, and can never be handled carelessly or ignorantly. However, because of the bomb hysteria, the danger has been exaggerated. Properly handled, they can be as safe as the gasoline in your car. After all, you wear an isotope of radium in your watch and are not harmed. Yet there is enough radiation from the luminous paint to produce serious trouble over a long period. The watch itself is a perfect shield. But you should never wear it face down.

At the Hanford works certainly enough isotopes have been handled to kill everyone in America, yet this plant has the highest industrial safety record in the State of Washington: injuries from radiation—none; major injuries per million man-hours—0.7. This is less than half the figure for offices in Seattle.

Knowing the dangers and guarding against them results in a better safety record than normal.

Isotopes are dangerous only because of their radiation. They won't burn, or explode, or corrode their way through containers—unless they are incorporated in chemicals that would do these things anyway. Safe handling for all is the same in kind, varying in degree with the type and strength of the radiation.

The low-level isotopes required for most industrial uses do not need elaborate protection. The whole basis for safety is to make sure that personnel *never* are exposed to more than the minimum safe amount of rays. The unit of human exposure is the *roentgen*, in honor of Wilhelm Konrad Roentgen, discoverer of X-rays. It is abbreviated simply as "r." In itself it is complex, giving a measure of the number of ionizations caused by a certain radiation in dry air in a unit of time. But its use is not complicated. There are instruments which read directly in r's, giving the total dose of radiation that is being received at a given point. All forms of activity are included—alphas, betas, gammas and X-rays.

A given dose of radiation is less dangerous if confined to one small part of the body, as in the case of dental X-rays, which measure 50r or more. But it can't often be repeated without harm, for the damage done is cumulative and permanent. That is why the dentist has you hold the X-ray film. If he exposed himself day after day, with one patient after another, he would soon accumulate a dose of radiation that would be dangerous, even fatal.

The roentgen is a unit of total exposure over a length of time. Thus the instruments that measure it "fill up" the way a pail fills up with water. AEC's Health Physics Department has ruled that a total exposure of 0.3r per week, the year round, is safe. Within limits you can take more for a short time. Hundreds of roentgens are given to cancer patients on a confined area of the body, but the total tolerance is soon reached.

The price of overexposure is, first, burns and ulcers, then deep physiological changes and finally death.

A group working with radiation takes these precautions: the rooms in which isotopes are used, or which isotope-workers frequent—including all washrooms, locker rooms, etc.—are constantly monitored for general radiation level in the air, in dust on all surfaces, in any liquid wastes. This is done with portable survey meters, which AEC specifies must be used wherever isotopes are present.

There is always some danger, of course, to the men working around a research reactor. Since the shielding has holes in it for inserting isotope material, though they are carefully plugged with lead, there can be leaks. The worst leaks are those that are too small to be detected but that can gradually raise the concentration of some deadly radioisotope in the air.

At Brookhaven some years ago the biologists noticed that hornets concentrate barium in their bodies. Someone suggested using them as leak detectors around the pile. A principal fission product inside is radiobarium. By keeping cages of hornets around the laboratory and watching them carefully for radioactivity, it proved possible to detect leaks long before they could be found by instruments alone.

Next, there are many kinds of protection—lead shields around "hot" operations, warning counters which ring bells when the roentgen level goes too high, interlocks on doors that prevent people entering rooms where dangerous levels exist. Finally, every member of the group is checked for the total amount of radiation he receives, usually on a daily basis. Visitors to radiation areas must undergo the same thing. People who work in the area regularly wear two types of monitoring device: a film badge and dosimeter. Temporary visitors wear them too.

The badge, which carries the wearer's name and employee number or address, is merely a small piece of unexposed X-ray film in a light-tight container that pins onto your coat. Every night, or at the end of the week, all badges are emptied and developed. If there is any darkening of the film, the worker who wore it is immediately summoned and examined by Geiger counter. If exposures were heavy, there may be blood and urine studies and possibly hospitalization. Exposure to dangerous radiation is not often received unwittingly. One who has had it immediately goes to the health physics people for medication and watching.

The dosimeter is handier. It is about the size and shape of a fountain pen and is worn in the same way. It is an ingenious form of electroscope, contained in an insulating tube. Inside is a thin quartz thread coated with metal. The device is charged by the monitoring department and if, as you wear it, radiation passes through it, the charge leaks away by ionization. In many instruments there is a small lens at one end. You look through it and see the image of the thread against a scale. Fully charged, it reads zero. A positive reading shows that you have received radiation.

Dosimeters are piled high at the entrances to "hot" labs; everyone takes one and clips it on, then forgets it. At the end of the day they are all turned in and read for radiation.

When I visited a "hot" area at Argonne, my guide and I stopped at the rack, put on dosimeters and rubbers (they don't want you tracking contaminated dust out of the laboratory). When we came out we checked the meters. There was also a monitoring gadget on the wall, with holes for hands and feet. We stood at this and watched a meter to see if our extremities had picked up anything. The machine worked improperly for my guide and showed exposure of one hand. Immediately he went to the health physics office and was carefully explored by a sensitive counter. He hadn't been contaminated; the machine had gone wrong. But this shows how important it is to track down any possible exposure at once.

When there is danger of radioactive dust in the air, workers put on special canvas suits. These are turned in at night and laundered. Sometimes masks have to be worn also. In one room at Hanford, where really deadly materials are handled, the operators crawl in through long plastic ducts attached to holes in the wall. The ducts are fastened, air-tight, to plastic suits in which the men work. Air from outside is gently pumped through the system, so that there is always positive pressure pushing any contamination *away* from the wearer. At the end of the job these Buck Rogers characters crawl back through their ducts, leaving the suits behind. If one has received appreciable radiation, he won't work there again till his total dose has fallen below the weekly average of 0.3 roentgen.

There was a story of a messenger employed at Oak Ridge in the war. His duty was to carry a small package from one building to another once a day—nothing else. A conscientious man, he offered to carry such packages all day to help win the war. He was turned down without explanation. Long afterward he found out that he had been carrying enough radiation in that one package to give him a whole day's safe exposure in a few minutes.

No such secrecy is necessary now; in fact, safety is a matter of such complete and detailed instructions that everyone has it on his mind all the time. The endless routine of changing clothes, clipping on badges and dosimeters, slipping in and out of rubbers, prevents a person from developing the familiarity that breeds contempt. You remember your radiation precautions as automatically as you look both ways before crossing a street. If a man does get careless, he soon loses his job.

When actually working with radioactive materials, shielding is the principal safeguard. You find it everywhere, from the vaults and potholes where incoming isotopes are stored, to the shielded delay tanks where wastes are held for "cooling." Quantities of lead bricks are stacked everywhere, for use in walling off dangerous experiments. These are four to six inches thick and dovetail together so as to leave no cracks.

From the beginning of work with isotopes during the war

it was known that they couldn't be handled directly. The ingenious remote control methods that were developed have created a new kind of engineering—the science of mechanical manipulators. In the "hot labs" or "caves," where isotopes are worked on, but where human beings never go, mechanical robots have to substitute for hands. The caves are usually totally enclosed areas whose lead-and-concrete walls are of less than room height. Arrangements of shafts and gears reach over these walls, with mechanisms at their ends for performing almost any operation upon a test tube, a bottle or the isotope itself. The operator stands outside, and with hand grips connected to the mechanism is able to initiate delicate manipulations within. He follows the remote-control motions through a series of mirrors.

In a more elaborate setup the cave is a roofed vault with yard-thick windows of solid lead glass or giant "fishbowls" of zinc bromide solution. These liquid sandwiches are better, because glass mysteriously turns black under strong radiation. However, researchers at Argonne are finding out why, and have developed a special cesium glass that stays transparent.

John Payne of G. E.'s Knolls Atomic Laboratory has devised many ingenious manipulators with metal fingers that can actually scratch a match or write the operator's name. But H. L. Hull and R. C. Goertz at Argonne have probably done most to improve the science of remote handling of dangerous materials. Their latest mechanisms are almost human—a complex of shafts, gears, servo-mechanisms and electronic devices, to which has been added "the human touch."

The "hot" end of the manipulator is a rough duplicate of the hand, with wrist motion, all degrees of elbow and shoulder freedom, as well as up-and-down and twisting movements. There are two rubber-sheathed rods for "fingers"; these are capable of doing anything the hand and arm can do, grasping, turning, pulling, pushing, corking and uncorking bottles, pouring, stirring—any action that is needed on the laboratory bench.

At the control end of the mechanism there is a grip for each hand—a pair of metal gloves, so to speak—into which you insert thumbs and forefingers. The gloves move freely **in**

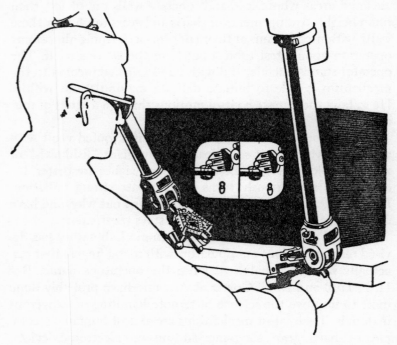

any direction, to any position you wish. You can squeeze, lift, lower, turn in all combinations, one hand or both, while watching the results through the safety window. It takes only a few minutes to get the hang of the gadget; even a novice can pick up a book of matches, tear one out and strike it, then flip it to put it out. You can pick up a glass of water, stir it with a rod, then pour it into another glass without spilling a drop. No doubt with a little practice you could tie a shoe.

Dr. Goertz's latest, the one he calls the "master-slave manipulator," is as intricate as a computing machine, which it somewhat parallels. In it are servos, potentiometers, linear differential transformers, torque converters and controllers and a lot more. Its master wrinkle is that it transmits, back to the operator, the sense of touch. You can *feel* what you are doing as well as see it. This lifelike touch greatly increases the ability of the machine to do ultradelicate manipulations where the amount of pressure or twist is important, as in handling thin glasswear or turning up small screws. After a little time with it you can easily imagine that the machine is not there at all, that your arms have actually become ten feet long and impervious to radiation.

The one feature still missing in these robots is proper viewing. Argonne scientists are now working on a three-dimensional TV unit to move your eyes up close to the work. With this laboratory-sized 3-D oufit the last barrier will have been lifted.

No matter how enthusiastic one gets over the marvels of electronics, one still has to admire even more the human mind, which can not only do everything a machine can do but can exercise judgment too.

AEC's Department of Health Physics, which inspires all of this protective equipment, is probably the largest single group devoting all its time to safety, in any industry. More than 500 people study radiation and its effects on the human body, methods of preventing exposure, treatment in case of exposure, the fixing of units of tolerance, and many other details. They have determined, for instance, that the lethal dose is from 400r to 600r, and that, in general, the effect of radiation is to destroy the blood and its ability to protect the body from infection. A great deal of their work is concerned with finding better antidotes for radiation that can be administered to whole populations during an atomic disaster. So far, not very much can be done for the exposed person but protect him with penicillin, transfusion and general hospital care.

The department deserves great credit for having made atomic work one of the safest of industrial pursuits. Though some hundreds of thousands work for the AEC or its contractors, radiation injuries are extremely rare and deaths from it almost unknown. Only four have so far died from overexposure. Compare this with the scores who died in the early days of X-rays, and the hundreds more who were permanently injured. It is a remarkable demonstration of the power of research to penetrate to the heart of a problem and solve it.

With these men and women looking out for you it is a good deal safer to buy and use radioisotopes than it would be to put into service a new company car.

PART THREE

Atoms Are
for All of Us

I. The Atom and Your Future

• • • • • • • • • • •

THE ATOMIC age will by no means offer opportunities only to large industry and topnotch scientists. There is a fabulous future in it for American talent in general, at all levels and in hundreds of different trades and professions. Never have our young people looked ahead to so much new territory to explore. All the way from engine operators to theoretical mathematicians, men of vigor are challenged to take charge of atomic energy in all its phases. Medicine, industry, agriculture will need tens of thousands of people for jobs that never existed before. In the technical fields engineers, chemists, geologists, metallurgists, designers, all will need to be reoriented. In research the frontiers will leap outward in many new directions. There is no predicting where voyages of discovery will lead.

For example, in the fission products industry: with reactors going everywhere on land and sea there will be a vast overflow of deadly isotopes to be gathered, concentrated, chemically treated and disposed of. Today only a small handful of men know how to do this; they have virtually taught themselves this complex job. Before many atomic power stations have gone on the line, there will be demand for hundreds of specially trained chemists and engineers; handlers, laboratory technicians, truckmen, electricians, Geigermen, health physics experts, and medical personnel. All for jobs that did not exist a few years before.

Imagine, too, the many skilled machinists, toolmakers and other shop talent who will be needed to build the reactors. Seldom before has such large machinery demanded so exacting a standard of precision. Apparatus which must not fail must be made by men capable of a new standard of workmanship.

On shipboard a new kind of "black gang" will be needed —all the way from the former furnace stoker, who will stand control-rod watches, to the chief, who will have to know as much of nuclear engineering as he now knows of steam. The whole engine-room force, on land or sea, will have to know the basic rules of health physics, the science of nuclear measurement; above all, what to do in case of a breakdown.

Every artisan and technician in the atomic field will have to be more skilled and better informed than artisans are now. He will have been to special schools and will no doubt have more education than many or most of the shop people today. For the demands of atomic energy are great and the penalty for failing them may be death.

On the engineering side the professions will sprout new specialties beyond count. At M.I.T. I once asked a professor in a pioneering field what he did for textbooks. "We have no textbooks," he replied. "Part of the course is to write one."

It will be this way in every branch of the new art: new courses, new territory to explore, textbooks that are obsolete almost before they are in print.

Undoubtedly the swing to atomic energy will put some people out of the jobs they now hold. Fewer will be working in coal mines, fewer on the railroads that now haul coal. But this technological unemployment is healthy and normal in America. Soon, the people who lose their jobs are snapped up by the new art, and with them thousands more.

Perhaps the most lively group in all the atomic world will be the inventors and researchers, with brand new forces and natural laws to work with. With the new Atomic Energy Act in force private individuals will be able to devise new gadgets, patent them, found companies on them, struggle with each other, sink or swim according to their skill and acumen. People with true scientific minds will soon be searching for new things to do with isotopes, new ways to make them do the intricate jobs of the world and do them better. Engineers with a flair for "cooking up" new machines will invent better methods of mining and refining the atomic metals, new ways to make heavy water, new cooling, new heat exchanging, new pumps. Let there be a great discovery, such as the application of hydrogen-helium to the making of power, and the field will become unlimited.

Look at an example or two of what the atomic age has already done. Dr. R. C. Goertz at Argonne Laboratory found that in handling heavy isotope shipments in the shop with an overhead crane it was difficult to keep the load from swinging like a pendulum. Ordinarily a rigger walks alongside, steadying the load. "Hot" objects can't be approached too closely. So Goertz invented a gadget to kill the swing.

It is an ingenious electronic device built into the crane carriage, controlling the driving motors in such a way that the first pendulum swing causes the carriage to "run after it," blotting it out. A control box on the floor permits a rigger to set a load down precisely where he wants it, with no backing and filling from above.

The antiswing crane was invented to fill a single need in the atomic laboratory. But it will have applications throughout industry. In thousands of shops the swing of heavy burdens is a troublesome problem nobody has ever solved. Especially where pots of red hot metal are carried, or explosives, or very delicate equipment, there is sure to be a place for this unexpected contribution from the atomic age.

One more example: A technician, working with a radioisotope of the rare earth thulium, noted that its radiation was in the X-ray rather than the gamma range (X-rays are longer than gammas). After some experiment he built a small portable unit carrying a tiny dab of thulium-170, that will produce X-rays of 100,000-volt energy for three or four months without recharging. The entire contrivance weighs less than ten pounds and is about the size of a big box of cigars.

This chance invention may have tremendous importance in medicine, completely outside the atomic field. A portable X-ray unit *without power supply* will be eagerly sought on the battlefield, in hospitals and in emergency stations during disasters. There is nothing remotely like it now. In industry, too, it can be used for radiographic work on light apparatus, where big standard machines are too large or too expensive to operate.

For the inventive mind there will hardly be a limit to the new ways in which atomic forces can be put to work. The question is, where shall we get the inventive minds for the atomic age? The answer is already in the making. AEC, spearheading the task, is doing its level best to help provide these minds. At Oak Ridge the commission sponsors an Institute of Nuclear Studies, presided over by 30 universities of the south. Here, six-week courses are given to those who already have a general technical training.

AEC also has educational arrangements with colleges and universities all over the land, sponsoring courses, financing research fellowships, contracting for investigations in physics, chemistry, biology and many more. The American Society for Engineering Education is helping in all this. So are hundreds of colleges and technical schools on their own. A vast process of reorientation is going on, to bring formal teaching up to atomic requirements.

Nor is this entirely on the advanced level. Science well knows that its talents start young, and that the search for eager young minds must begin at least in high school. A recent visit to a school Science Fair proved to me that the teen-agers of the nation are well ahead of their elders in atomic interest. There were literally dozens of exhibits, some from boys and girls of 15 or younger, built around atomic energy. Recording Geiger counters (that worked), models of reactors, demonstrations of isotopes and of the elements—all showed that the youth of today is thinking in terms of the atoms he hopes to control tomorrow.

Gerrit G. Zwart of Suffern High School in New York, is a typical leader in the drive toward atomic understanding at high-school level. In a recent issue of the government's *School Life* magazine, he says: "My students and I are somewhat impatient with the layman's lack of interest (in atomic energy). We have a consuming conviction that, whether he likes it or not, we are all enmeshed in a fantastic framework of fate . . . like a fly caught in a spider web."

Mr. Zwart has set up an Atomic Energy Club in his school.

Study of the subject is required in the senior year. The kids build models of piles, work with mild isotopes, go on field trips which include the Brookhaven Laboratory and other AEC facilities near by.

And what of the teachers themselves? Among them the interest is fully as great. In a number of states science teachers are being invited to summer schools of the atom for basic training. The material they get goes straight back to the classroom; in fact, the official curricula are beginning to include it. Everywhere that there are government atomic plants, there is sure to be accelerated teacher interest, which is not only handed on to the youngsters but to their parents as well. Many an adult evening class today is wrestling with the problems of fission and learning how atomic power will be achieved.

America is awake to the atomic age. Atoms are for everybody. Whether they are to be destroyers or builders of life, is for the people themselves to decide—by training, by thought, by the substitution of knowledge for ignorance.

"The essence of science," says R. J. Blakely, of the U.S. Office of Education, "does not lie in its products, either for good or for ill. It lies in an attitude and a method—the attitude of 'methodic doubt,' the refusal to accept any proposition merely on authority; the method of critical analysis, hypothesis, observation, experiment and verification."

There is a message there for us all.

2. Interim
• • • •

ATOMS FOR PEACE was written two years ago, at the
dawn of what is now most certainly the Atomic Age. If anyone still doubted then that the atom would become a major
force in our daily lives, he cannot doubt it further. We had
seen some ten years of careful, rather fumbling progress, in
which atomic scientists and engineers were busy groping in
the dark for methods of capturing the energy of fission. Most
of this time was spent in breaking new ground. There were
few standardized applications of atomic energy; it was largely
pioneering. We can look back on this as the "Decade of Experiment."

Now we are past that, and have embarked upon a tremendously accelerated period—a "Decade of Test." At this
writing, atomic energy is still not ready to take over human
burdens, but it has signified that it will. We are in the stage
of inventing the "hardware" which will reduce earlier experiment to practical and reliable machines.

It is no more possible now to give the last word than it
was then. There will probably follow a "Decade of Slow Acceptance;" no doubt, after that there will be other decades
of trial and change, improvement and expansion. However,
by 1975, we should be pretty well oriented to the atom, and
making use of most of its enormous potential. This added
chapter, therefore, is in the nature of an interim report, partly

to corroborate the findings of the main book and partly to prognosticate still further what is in store.

The great milestone which has been set up since the last writing was the International Conference on the Peaceful Uses of Atomic Energy at Geneva, Switzerland, in August, 1955. The world did not go to this meeting with too much hope, but it came out of it afire with enthusiasm. Geneva seems to have been the turning point; seventy-three nations participated; all seem to have resolved to go home and get to work in earnest.

The very great contribution of Geneva was that all nations were suddenly made aware that they could work as a unit in harnessing the atom for constructive purposes. And further, that the best way to reduce the deadly threat of annihilation held over us by Atoms for War, was to make every possible advance with Atoms for Peace. These three magic words have become a rallying cry for all the world. What is needed now— and resolutely sought—is, in the vivid phrase of Admiral Rickover, a "crash program" for nuclear peace, an all-out drive not too different from that other crash program which opened Pandora's box and revealed the Bomb. Not too different in devotion and energy and money, but far different in purpose. This is, without question, the only way in which the threat of wholesale destruction can really be downed.

At Geneva, it was as if the sun had suddenly begun to shine on a storm-wracked earth, bringing to sudden sprouting seeds that had lain long dormant. Some of the first results of this sprouting we shall see in the next few pages.

Immediately upon news of the success at Geneva, the Joint Committee on Atomic Energy in Congress set forth on a new program, intended at least to double our participation in atomic development. Many of the members of the Committee had learned to their amazement at Geneva that other countries were also far advanced in atomic thinking. They had learned that a vast "atomic pool" was to be established in western Europe. They had learned that Russia was far along in an over-all drive toward atomic power. They had learned that England, in spite of her many difficulties in the past few years, fully intended to be a world leader in substituting the atom for conventional fuels.

The U.S. Atomic Energy Commission let no time be wasted in clearing the decks. Within a month they began to highlight their Power Demonstration Reactor Program, announced the previous January. As a new phase of its original Five-Year Reactor Program, which we have described, this actively sought to shift the burden of testing atomic power to private interests. If atomic power was to become an everyday source of energy for America, it must be tried out under everyday conditions.

Electrical manufacturing and operating companies responded immediately, and in the months that have passed since, we have seen a tremendous surge of interest express itself in actual plans for private atomic power-station building. To do this has required a very long view, both on the part of the government and of the electrical industry. For almost every station now on the drawing boards will be at least partially obsolete by the time it is in use. This is the essence of the crash program: *Don't wait. Try now!* This is the best thing that could happen to atomic power, because, under the duress of actual conditions, advances are made much more surely and more rapidly than when tentative experiments in miniature sizes are relied upon exclusively.

The main difference between the original Five-Year Program and the Power Demonstration plan is that private industry will now pay the bills. This has the important advantage that, under competitive conditions, the incentive to go ahead

rapidly is much greater. If anyone doubts this, take a look at
the plants already scheduled for immediate construction.

First there is the Duquesne Light Company's Shippingport plant, now nearing completion and to be ready for generating at least 60,000 kilowatts of electricity for Pittsburgh
in 1957. Next we have a mammoth station to be erected by
the Commonwealth Edison Company near Chicago. This
will be the first atomic station wholly financed with private
capital, and will cost about $45 million. Service is expected
from it by 1960.

An interesting reversal of the usual cautious approach to
large pioneer construction should be noted here. General Electric, which signed the contract to build Commonwealth's big
plant in July, 1955, has now, eight months later, contracted
with Pacific Gas & Electric Company to build a small atomic
station near San Francisco, which will be the *pilot plant* for the
huge one in Chicago. It will be completed and ready to go in
one year, with a tiny contribution of 5000 kilowatts. The unusual point about it is that the large enterprise was undertaken
before the small one that is to prove that the large one is
feasible.

A tabulation of other large plants in prospect looks like a
forest of great redwood trees. There is the comparatively small
unit for the Consumer's Public Power District of Nebraska
—75,000 kilowatts; the Detroit Edison Associates' plant at
100,000; the Yankee Atomic Electric Company's station of
134,000 in western Massachusetts; Pennsylvania Power and
Light's big powerhouse of 150,000; and the giant of them all,
Consolidated Edison's Indian Point atomic colossus, at 250,000
kilowatts, for New York City. Nearly all of them will be running in 1960.

Two are special, for their builders have taken a leap into
the future and have staked many millions on principles still in

experiment. Most notable is the Nebraska job, which will be a "fast breeder." It will be remembered that the breeder, which actually makes more uranium fuel than it receives, was the idea of Walter H. Zinn of the AEC. His pioneering spirit has been richly rewarded in this use of what will probably become the most economical type of atom plant. It is through breeding that we shall avoid the enormous cost of separating fissionable U-235 from "useless" U-238, 139 times as abundant.

While intense activity is springing up all over the world in atomic power stations, development of atomic transportation has gone quietly ahead, with much success. The U.S. Submarine *Nautilus*, described in previous pages, has amounted to an engineering wonder of the world. She has already traveled more than 25,000 miles, mostly under water, and has shown herself superior in many ways to the most optimistic hopes. One of her phenomenal runs was a single submerged journey of 1300 miles from New London, Conn., to Puerto Rico. Her sistership, the *Sea Wolf*, whose hull was launched about a year ago, will soon be ready for sea trials. A more advanced type of atomic reactor, using liquid sodium metal, will probably make her faster and more efficient than the *Nautilus*.

Success with atomic subs has speeded up the work on many other types of conveyance. A giant prototype power plant known as the "LSR" is now being built by Westinghouse to work out the problems of atomic propulsion for very large ships. Since this is a military project, not very much is yet known about it. There is less secrecy to the Army's "package Power Reactor," which will be a very small unit mounted in trucks, for great mobility. This plant on wheels, presumably the first of its kind in the world, will be ready by the middle of 1957. It will turn out about 1800 kilowatts and will undoubtedly open the way for civilian mobile units for use in disaster areas and for remote places where fuel is prohibitively expensive.

One other military atomic project which is sure to have great influence of peacetime uses is the atomic aircraft, under study at the National Reactor Testing Station at Arco, Idaho. About all that the government will say about this is that the program has been accelerated and that it shows promise. One can expect to see an atomic plane in the sky, possibly, by 1960. The major difficulty in using atoms in the air is the necessity for enormous weights of shielding to protect personnel. While absolutely nothing official has been said about recent work in this field, a persistent rumor suggests that there may be another way to effect human protection than to use brute weight and bulk. If this should turn out to be so, there will be an immediate rush to put atomic airliners into the sky. Judging from the extraordinary technical discoveries of the past five years, it is more than likely that atomic air travel will be a fact, say, in the next 15 years.

As we go on increasing our use of uranium for fuel, the "ashes" problem, of course, becomes more and more threatening. Nothing particularly new has been discovered in methods of fission-product disposal. The practice continues of burying the material out of harm's way, leaving it in deeply hidden tanks in liquid solutions till it "cools off." So far, only military and experimental wastes are being produced. But when, in 1960, a million or more kilowatts of commercial atomic power begin to flow, the disposal problem may well become acute. According to Dr. L. P. Hatch of the Brookhaven National Laboratory, annual fission wastes, by the end of the century, may reach the staggering radioactive equivalent of 400,000 tons of radium. This is something like 100 million times the radioactivity given off by all the refined radium in the world today.

It is unthinkable that atomic power should be under development all over the world at the rate contemplated, without confidence that this gigantic "garbage disposal" problem can be solved. There is, indeed, definite confidence in this direction. Fission products will not necessarily be regarded as waste, but as tremendously valuable by-products, capable of realizing a wholly new service from the atom. Not only do they furnish huge quantities of radioactive rays of great value to research and to medicine; they turn out vast quantities of *heat*. It will not be heat that you can safely employ in your home. Under proper industrial control, however, "sinks" of fission products can be employed to run factories, even to generate electricity on their own.

The radioactivity of fission products is already being used in many experiments, such as the production of industrial X-rays, the speeding up of oil-refining processes, and in food and drug sterilization. This last has gone ahead to a practical stage already, and now seems likely to establish a huge new industry of its own.

So important an advance is radiation sterilization of food, to eliminate costly refrigeration, that both the Army Quartermaster's Corps and the Department of Agriculture are pushing research vigorously. The Congressional Joint Committee has held several hearings on it, bringing to light very promising progress. All types of radiation can be used: Van de Graaff generators, betatrons, linear accelerators, X-rays, radioisotopes specially made, and fission products. The latter are by far the cheapest, but it is still too soon to know whether the mixed radiation given off by many different atoms can be tolerated. There is a rather narrow range of energies that can be used on foods without destroying flavor or causing destruction of the product itself. It seems safe to say that fission materials will eventually be used almost entirely, since it will probably be possible to select the useful "hot" isotopes from the gross waste by an automatic chemical process—an extension of the present practice at the Hanford plutonium plant. The main question is an economic one: can these isotopes be produced cheaply enough to compete with other forms of radiation?

The single example of the irradiation of seed potatoes shows how important this new field is. Agricultural experts say that if it had been possible to treat the potato surpluses that glutted government storehouses a few years ago, they could have been distributed and used. As it was, enormous quantities spoiled in storage and had to be destroyed. A year or two more will undoubtedly see standardized radiation treatment of many farm products, as well as grains, cotton, and so forth, during routine handling operations. Similarly, a good many perishable drugs can be made permanently sterile by irradiating them. Penicillin is an example already in use. Such critical drugs as the Salk vaccine will probably follow soon.

It seems certain that fission wastes will be fully used in the future; many laboratories are busy now finding outlets for them. An important application will be for luminous-dial watches and clocks, as well as for signs, tags, buttons, meter hands and the like, to show up in the dark. The radium salts used now are very expensive. Much work has been done on "permanently excited" fluorescent lamps, which contain small amounts of radioactive material to keep them ionized. Thus they can be lighted immediately on turning the switch, without condensers or transformers. It will undoubtedly be found that X-rays can be generated by some fission products. This means built-in radiation sources like the thulium isotope described earlier in the book. Still another use, which may turn out to be among the most important, is in "hot" chemistry. No one can say yet what can happen here. It has already been found that radiation will hasten certain reactions in the catalytic cracking of petroleum, and that some plastics can be improved by it. The field of organic chemistry is tremendous. Radiation-induced reactions will be giving us synthesized materials not obtainable in any other way.

Atomic energy continues to aid medicine. At the Brookhaven National Laboratory the use of the neutron treatment for tumors has reached a firm basis, experimentally, after a rather unpromising start. The neutrons, directed upon a tumor deep inside the body, generate radiation lethal to the growth without damaging intervening tissue. A quite different use of atomic energy, being made by the Bronx Veteran's Hospital in New York, offers a quick, effective method of studying heart action in cardiac patients. A minute amount of a radioisotope is injected, and a bedside machine then measures its distribution in the arterial blood. A Geiger counter, electronic equipment, oscillo-scope and camera produce permanent photographic records of a patient's condition in about six minutes.

An important milestone is the special medical atomic reactor now in its testing stage at the University of California at Los Angeles. It was built by North American Aviation, Inc., and is the world's first, specifically built for cancer therapy. This machine, designed to produce gamma rays and slow or "thermal" neutron beams, can turn out about five kilowatts of energy. The gamma radiation is equal to that of 50 pounds of radium. UCLA's reactor, which will not be ready for public use until 1957, will exploit the very important Brookhaven discoveries in neutron therapy. It has been found that neutrons, in connection with certain chemical injections, have a very high selectivity for diseased tissue. This is perhaps the beginning of the "breakthrough" which thousands of laboratory scientists have sought for years: a *specific* for cancer.

From what we have seen, in the field of atomic power and radioisotope application, it must be evident that the world intends to exploit the atom to the full, and will soon be using vast quantities of uranium. But what of the supply of the metal itself? Are earlier hopes of great abundance to be realized? Only eight years ago northern Canada, Czechoslovakia and the Belgian Congo produced the only substantial quantities of uranium in the world. Most mining experts thought this was about all that would be found. Today, owing to a tremendous advance in the technology of uranium discovery, it is turning out that the North American continent may have a bonanza of uranium surpassing the other three combined.

One of the largest bodies of ore ever unearthed was discovered in New Mexico in 1955 and was named the Jackpile Mine. A hundred million tons of carnotite have so far been located and no one knows the extent of the deposit. Meanwhile, the Canadians have had amazing luck in the region of Ontario north of Lake Huron. Three years ago the Blind River district showed weak signs of surface uranium. Today, a lightly buried ore body of 100,000,000 tons has been staked out and it is expected that this is only the beginning. The Blind River field, says AEC's uranium expert, Jesse C. Johnson, may prove to be the world's largest. It should be very comforting for Americans to realize that, in the coming Atomic Age, we shall certainly not lack for home-grown supplies.

Let us end this interim account with one more "tall one." It is now rather generally believed that uranium may some day be unnecessary. There is real hope that atomic *fusion*—the terrifying heart of the hydrogen bomb—may be tamed to furnish power. If this occurs, a great host of light metals, perhaps even the hydrogen from water itself, may be made to yield their incredible supply of stored energy. In that case, the world would at last be free of any possible fear that fuel could ever fail.

The first official news that science was on the trail of

peaceful atomic fusion came in an announcement by Dr. Homi J. Bhabha, the Indian delegate who presided at the Geneva Conference. It turned out that the AEC had for some time been exploring the subject, under the designation Project SHERWOOD. Dr. Bhabha said that he felt certain the fusion-for-peace problem would be solved within twenty years.

The fusion of the very light atoms of hydrogen into helium produces staggering temperatures, estimated to be some hundreds of millions of degrees. The problem of using such temperatures is the main one. No one, to date, has publicly suggested how it can be done, yet the scientists of AEC, especially Dr. Edward Teller, the genius behind the H-Bomb, would not be making serious investigations if they did not think there was hope of success. "Our work is in the research stage," Admiral Strauss of AEC has stated, "and many years of intensive effort may be required before the first prototype of an operating thermo-nuclear machine may be developed."

Perhaps. But notice what has happened in a single ten-year span, since the end of World War II. In 1945 few engineers expected to live to see practical atomic power; still fewer geologists thought there was enough uranium in the world to make the Atomic Age possible. Who knows at what moment some tiny light, shining on a fluorescent screen, may open the way, suddenly, to limitless energy almost for nothing?

3. Open Seas Ahead

● ● ● ● ● ● ● ● ●

SINCE THIS book was first published a decade ago, atomic energy has gone into high gear. The strides that have been made are fantastic. Never before has a great discovery become a major force for good around the world in its first twenty years. Yet the tremendous advance of the atomic art has been no real surprise to nuclear scientists and engineers. Progress has, instead, been an orderly unfolding of a new technology, predicted from the beginning by the experts and to some extent reflected in the pages of this book. In a few brief paragraphs let us examine what has happened and what further promises are in store.

In nuclear power plants, as predicted, the Shippingport station came first. It went critical for the first time in 1957 and has been operating steadily ever since, supplying electricity to the great city of Pittsburgh. Not very many users even know that they live with atomic power.

During these eight years more than a dozen large plants have been built in the United States and many more are planned. Today, in 1965, nuclear-generated electricity is just about competitive with fossil fuel energy. In another 20 years it is expected that half the power plants in America will be nuclear. There are many designs. Backed by AEC research, utility companies and reactor makers are rapidly refining and improving a diversity of types, many now using plutonium instead of uranium. Small, high-efficiency units are popping up in the suburbs of cities all over the land. They are absolutely safe. A nuclear plant cannot blow up.

The atom is even more valuable under the sea. With the building of a large American nuclear fleet of submarines, many of which are Polaris type missile carriers, the atom is taking over our submarine navy. It is also driving surface ships. The gigantic carrier Enterprise (CVAN-65), the world's largest vessel, is driven by the largest nuclear plant on earth. And the Navy has two other atomic craft: a cruiser and a frigate. Eventually all major naval ships will be nuclear driven. For several years now the U.S. Maritime Commission has been operating the world's first nuclear freighter-passenger ship, the *Savannah*. She can voyage more than 336,000 miles—13 times around the world—on a single charge of fuel.

Nuclear power in the air and in space are no longer dreams. Small plutonium-driven electric generators are carried in advanced satellites. Larger nuclear engines have been tested that can lift rockets. Against the judgment of the military the promising nuclear-driven supersonic bomber was postponed; it probably should not have been, for there are reliable reports that the Soviet Air Force has many such planes in service.

Great interest is developing in the controlled fusion reaction—the "tamed" hydrogen bomb. But the difficulties imposed by multi-million-degree temperatures may require years of research into materials and methods of containing the reaction before real power can be generated. Nevertheless, a hydrogen-to-helium fusion demonstration has been presented by General Electric daily at the New York World's Fair. The bang is loud and dramatic, though it lasts hardly a billionth of a second. Yet it assures us that this "powerhouse of the sun" will some day be as controllable as uranium fission is now. When it is, a vast new ocean of power will be available to the world, probably using heavy hydrogen recovered from the oceans themselves. The supply is virtually inexhaustible.

Both fission and fusion are bound to play key roles in space. For long voyages among the planets no other energy source can compete.

On the horizon hovers a remarkable new development: the direct conversion of atomic heat into electricity by means of plasmas. Models have been built that can drive an electric fan. As full-scale machinery is invented our relatively cumbersome power plants of today, with their steam turbines and rotating electric generators, will go. With virtually no moving parts, such plants will turn out cheap electricity indeed.

Although the application of atomic energy to medicine and agriculture is slower than in the power field, it is steadily advancing. Cobalt-60 radiation is fast taking over from X-rays; every day radioactive isotopes are used in hospitals around the world for cancer therapy. And in research the "tagged" atom has become a standard tool in biology, physics, chemistry, metallurgy and in automated machinery in hundreds of industries. The dating of objects of great antiquity by natural isotopes has become the method of choice, because of its accuracy. Recently the new potassium-argon technique brought to light the age of one of the earliest human skulls. It was nearly two million years old!

A peaceful use for the untamed hydrogen bomb has been found: the digging of great canals, the moving of mountains, the deepening of harbors. The cutting of a sea-level canal from the Gulf of Mexico to the Pacific—a prohibitively costly undertaking by standard methods—will soon be possible by using specially designed fission-fusion explosives. Fallout, the one thing that still holds it back, will first have to be eliminated.

Such a canal, AEC says, can be dug for as little as one-tenth as much as with old-style explosives and conventional earth-moving equipment. The new excavator bomb will not only dig the hole but will carry the earth and rock out and dump them so that they never need be handled again.

One interesting wrinkle on the verge of trial is the nuclear water desalting plant. The shortage of fresh water has become so acute in the United States and many other parts of the world, that gigantic installations will be built as soon as designs and pilot plants can be prepared. The idea is to combine nuclear-electric generation with evaporating systems, the two sharing the atomic heat to produce thousands of kilowatts of electricity and at the same time millions of gallons of fresh water, not to mention tons of valuable marine salts. This will undoubtedly be the answer to thirsty cities like Los Angeles.

And there are many more uses on the way. If, behind it all there still lurks the terrible threat of the megaton bomb, this is not the fault of the atom but of the imperfection of man himself. To live in the world of the future men must be tough and clear-eyed and resolute. For it is not nature but man himself who must protect him from the misuses of his own ingenuity.

Useful Reading on the Atom
· · · · · · · · · · ·

Report on the Atom, by Gordon Dean. Knopf, 1953

The New Force, by Ralph E. Lapp. Harper & Bros., 1953

The Atomic Submarine and Admiral Rickover, by Clay Blair. Holt, 1954

Atomic Power Development and Private Enterprise: Hearings Before the Congressional Joint Committee on Atomic Energy. Government Printing Office, 1953

Radiation Monitoring in Atomic Defense, by D. E. Gray and J. H. Martens. Van Nostrand, 1951

Explaining the Atom, by Selig Hecht. Viking, 1947

Young People's Book of Atomic Energy, by Robert D. Potter. Dodd Mead, 1948

The Hell Bomb, by William L. Laurence. Knopf, 1951

Atomic Energy for Military Purposes, by Henry DeW. Smyth. Princeton University Press, 1945

Modern Arms and Free Men, by Vannevar Bush. Simon & Schuster, 1949

Sourcebook on Atomic Energy, by Samuel Glasstone. Van Nostrand, 1950

Prospecting for Uranium (Atomic Energy Commission and U.S. Geological Survey). Government Printing Office, 1949

Prospecting With a Counter, by Robert J. Wright. Government Printing Office, 1953

Atomic Science, Bombs and Power, by David Dietz. Dodd, Mead, 1954

Index
• • •